# THANK YOU CANCER

# THANK YOU CANCER

A MEMOIR: FROM "WHY ME?" TO "TEACH ME!"

BY

CARRIE H. PASCH

Copyright © 2022 Carrie H. Pasch

Cover Design: Chyntia Puspitasari
Photographer: Hannah Dougan
Interior Layout: Christina Hicks
ISBN13: 979-8986943848
PB

*All'amore della mia vita…*

# FOREWORD

Teachable, thankful, grateful; none of these words seem fitting in the same sentence as the dreaded six letter word cancer. In fact when I first heard this story for the first time, I felt myself wanting to jump on the defensive for this extraordinary woman who was facing something so devastating. Why does she need to be teachable and grateful, I wondered. Shouldn't she be allowed to just focus on healing and surviving? But then I met Carrie— and then I listened; really listened to her heart, her faith, her story— and I understood why these words fit perfectly.

None of us are promised an absence of problems, pain or trials. However, we are promised that God will take everything meant for evil and turn it for our good. Carrie Pasch learned to live this promise to its fullest, through good times, and painful ones.

You may not be facing cancer, but chances are you are

facing some unfair or overwhelming circumstances. Part of being human is facing challenges, but part of being a follower of Jesus is seeing the good, even when you are facing something devastating.

I can't wait for you to read *Thank You Cancer*. I can't wait for your faith to be ignited and hope to flood through your soul. And my prayer for you is that you will also remain teachable through this incredible journey of gratitude.

—Wendy Perez

# TABLE OF
# CONTENTS

# CHAPTER
# ONE

*II* Beach waves please," I said, sliding into the honey-colored, leather salon chair.

"Of course," my stylist responded, heating up the curling iron. "I know your go to by now."

"Thank you so much for squeezing me in today," I said after looking around. The salon was busy for 6:00PM on a Wednesday night in Red Bank, New Jersey, so I was happy to have secured an appointment with my busy travel schedule in the coming days. Blowouts not only reduced my morning prep time by half when I was on the road, they also made me feel polished and put together for my day of business meetings.

As she blew my shoulder-length blonde locks, I decided

to make use of the time to answer some work emails and review my upcoming travel itinerary. I had a big week in front of me, as my husband and I, owners of a digital marketing agency specializing in the automotive sector, would be traveling to Napa Valley, California to host one of our annual work events for a few hundred people.

Over the next thirty minutes, I worked efficiently through the list of unopened emails from event attendees and sponsors, and after taking a moment to pause and glance at the progress in the mirror, I found that my stylist had already swapped out the blow-dryer for the curling iron and was artfully sculpting the last few pieces of hair to achieve the perfectly styled beach-wave look: wrapping a thin, straight section of hair around the hot, metal barrel of the curling iron, and after a few seconds against the heat, unraveling the hair and gently tugging at the bottom tip to transform the kinky, tight curl into a relaxed, smooth wave.

As she sprayed extra-hold hair spray, I already felt my mood had revitalized, and my outfit— a basic yoga pant and white tee— had somehow seemed glamorized. I smiled, feeling thankful for the comfort of the salon chair as my happy place, paid, and headed to my car.

As I got situated, syncing the Bluetooth with my phone, I clicked on the Radio Italia App, on my iPhone and opened the Kiss Kiss Italia station to stream live, Italian music as I drove back to my parent's house in Rumson. Transporting myself back to Italy, the country that held a special place in my heart not only because Brian and I had been married there, but because it had allowed me to discover my inner designer fashionista, which had been in my DNA ever since I was a little girl.

Over the years, Brian and I had made it a point to travel to Italy a few times every year – to visit friends, family, and our house in Tuscany – and I noticed how the more time I spent there, the greater my desire became to delve deeper into learning the language.

As I coasted to a red light, the first few beats sounded to one of the earliest Italian songs I had learned. I smiled, recollecting the time I had visited my cousin in Abruzzo and how we sang this song together, out loud, in his car. So, without hesitation, I turned up the volume and started singing the words to *Piccoli Miracoli* by Tiromancino.

A few minutes later, as I was pulling into my parent's driveway, I realized how I had understood every word I was singing, and I couldn't help but reflect on how far I had come over the years regarding my fluency with the Italian language. Moreover, I thought about how my ongoing commitment to master the language had opened many doors for my personal ministry in Italy, motivating me to publish books, speak at events, and record video devotional messages for my

YouVersion Bible App, channel, all in Italian. The more these opportunities presented themselves, the more I was inspired to further pursue the subject of biblical studies.

Thinking of this, I realized my grades were probably posted on the Southeastern University platform and was eager to get inside my parent's house and see my marks. I dashed inside, grabbed my computer, and sat at the kitchen island, all the while thinking how comical it was that I was a student again.

I could vividly remember the excitement I had in my early twenties, as I graduated early from Gettysburg College to start my job in the fashion industry in New York City. Plans to go back to school had not been part of my future life agenda, especially plans to obtain a degree in the area of religious studies, but here I was, fifteen plus years later going back to school for my Masters of Divinity degree. Furthering my education in this area of studies, not only strengthened my personal faith, which I cultivated as an adult in my thirties, but it deepened my knowledge of biblical studies as I sought to serve and inspire others.

With no new grades posted, I decided to shut down my computer and finish a reading assignment before eating dinner with the family and heading to bed.

As the evening winded down, I said good night to my parents and went upstairs to complete my nightly skin routine and to ensure everything was organized in my suitcase for our early departure the following morning.

I checked to make sure my mask was in my purse, though I couldn't help but cringe at the idea of having to wear it during the entire duration of the flight. I understood the mandate, it just made the whole in-flight experience seem a little longer and more uncomfortable. "Oh, well," I told myself, "Don't stress, the world will hopefully be back to normal soon."

I got into bed and laid my head on my pillow, carefully lifting my hair and splaying it out onto the pillowcase like the shape of a handheld fan, in order to preserve the blowout. I sighed a breath of contentment as I relaxed in bed and allowed the cool sheets to settle over my body.

What I didn't know was just how far from normal my life would become in less than a week.

\*\*\*

On July 22, 2021, my morning started out like any other ordinary summer day while visiting my parents in the quaint, central, shore neighborhood where I grew up: Rumson, New Jersey. I got up, put on my comfortable Lululemon lounge wear, brushed my teeth, and glanced in the mirror to make sure my hair was still intact from the previous day's blowout, then meandered down to the kitchen.

After making a decaf, almond milk latte from our Nespresso machine, I sat down in my favorite leather club chair, and grabbed my journal. For me, journaling was one of my most important practices: my key in obtaining a positive perspective while navigating throughout the day. Each day, I established my perspective by writing down three things I was grateful for. I had found it to be such a simple yet powerful practice, because the more I postured my heart to see all the blessings and abundant ways God was working in my life, when difficult times presented themselves, the more I found myself already in the habit of focusing on the positive and fixed on what was good, right, and true.

That fateful morning, after recording three things I was grateful for, I prayed, read my Bible, then switched gears to tackle schoolwork for my master's degree. The first few hours of each day were sacred to me, as they are my most productive and creative window of time, especially for writing. It was common to find me wrapped in a blanket, feet propped up on the ottoman, typing into my laptop for hours at a time. My parents and husband poked fun at me for "never leaving my chair," but the truth was that my morning routine was so comfortable, productive, therapeutic, and it had become one of my favorite parts of the day.

As I was finishing up a school paper, my phone rang

with an unrecognizable, out of state number. I hesitated in answering thinking it was a telemarketer but then considered it could be a business call, so I picked up. The person on the other line said they were calling from my insurance company and had the authorization code for my upcoming breast MRI. I responded by explaining how they must have the wrong person because I do not have an upcoming MRI. I immediately thought it was a scam and went to hang up, when the woman on the other end said one thing that caught my attention: she asked me if I wanted the authorization code anyway. I agreed and told her that I would write it down then call my doctor to see if this was valid.

After I hung up the phone, I remember thinking to myself how that was one of the strangest calls I had ever received. Never in my life have I had my insurance company call me, out of the blue, and give me an approval code. It is usually the opposite. That was the moment I knew something was wrong.

I sat in my chair, took in the silence of the house, and stared out the kitchen window across the room. It was in that moment that I felt God trying to speak to me through that insurance representative, and more importantly, the moment I felt Him ask me: "How are you going to respond?" Was I going to ignore the sign and dismiss the call as something random and false, or was I going to listen and proactively address the situation? I thought about the two options, then scrolled through my contact list and dialed my doctor.

Miraculously, she was available to speak to me. My doctor explained that even though my mother had a non-genetic form of breast cancer, and I am still young (under forty years old), I was doing the right thing by conducting early detection screenings every six months (alternating between mammograms and MRIs). She continued to say that my next MRI screening was scheduled in two months, but she wanted to submit the papers to insurance in advance, just in case I wanted to go earlier than planned. She knew I had a busy travel schedule and wanted me to have flexibility with scheduling. I thanked her for all her help and hung up the phone.

My initial intuition, or what I'd begun to refer to as the whisper of the Holy Spirit signaling that something was wrong, was still lingering deep inside me. I had started to see that while it takes time to become familiar with hearing all the ways God's Spirit is trying to speak: sometimes it was through a small tug at the heart or a specific thought I couldn't quite shake from my mind; or sometimes it was as clear as a giant punch in the gut. Whichever form His voice embodied, I had developed an acute ear for that internal whisper that resided deep within me. So, once again, I found myself listening to it, and inhaling a long, deep breath, and exhaling slowly, I dialed the number to the Jacqueline M. Wilentz Breast Center at Monmouth Medical Center in Long Branch, New Jersey to see if they could schedule an MRI before I left for Florida the following week.

The MRI facility was fully booked with only one appointment available the next day at 6:00am, the time slot no one wanted, but without hesitation, I took it. Within twenty-four hours, I had the test completed and was meeting with the radiologist to review the results.

The images showed what appeared to be a six-millimeter tumor, the radiologist explained, the approximate size of a pea, within the upper quadrant of my right breast.

My head spun at the mention of the word tumor. My mother, who had come to accompany me for support, gave me a sympathetic "everything will be alright" look, as I think we both flashed back to her diagnosis: Estrogen-related invasive ductal carcinoma. Memories of helping her through her post-operative recovery came flooding back: routinely emptying her drains, time stamping her medication charts, and maintaining normal house chores she wasn't able to do.

Sensing my shock, she interjected into the conversation on my behalf and started to ask the doctor questions. For a moment, I found myself staring at the black and white images on the computer monitors and the voices around me became silent. After that split second, I snapped back to reality and proceeded to ask the doctor for the recommended next steps.

With the definitive conclusion that the first one would be a breast biopsy, I called a close family friend who worked in the medical field and asked if he would be willing to connect me with a radiology specialist to conduct the procedure. He was happy to help and put me in touch with a great doctor that squeezed me into her busy calendar early one morning. She was excellent, and the biopsy procedure which included the attachment of a micro-chip tracker onto my tumor, was quick and painless. I was grateful for her kindness and expertise, and thanked God for placing me into her skillful hands.

After that procedure, my husband and I decided to return to our home in Florida for a long weekend. It had been a whirlwind of a week in New Jersey, and we both agreed that it would be good for me to have a change of pace, see my friends, spend time at our house, and experience a sense of normalcy.

Brian had not only been such an incredible source of support and encouragement for me over the years but had also had learned the importance of obeying my intuition whispers. If I mentioned the phrase: "I just have a feeling," he knew not to doubt me. Whether it was a trip I somehow knew would get canceled, or a person that I predicted would betray me, or a business deal I guaranteed would not come to fruition, we had both learned not to ignore my internal voice and intuition.

With our masks on, boarding passes in hand, and carry-on bags by our side, we anxiously boarded the plane to Florida.

Within forty-eight hours of my biopsy, just before leaving to go out to dinner, my phone rang, and it was my breast doctor. I immediately clicked the speaker button, because I wanted Brian on the call as an extra set of ears.

In her soft, sympathetic voice, the doctor explained how the biopsy confirmed that I had both invasive ductal carcinoma and ductal carcinoma in situ.

Unlike my mother's cancer, mine was estrogen negative. It was also progesterone negative, and HER2 negative, signaling Triple Negative Breast Cancer (TNBC). As my doctor continued to recite the definition of my diagnosis, my brain was at maximum capacity with the mention of the words: cancer and invasive. I could only retain fragments of her sentences:

*Invasive refers to the cancer growing beyond its original location…ductal refers to the location… carcinoma refers to the cancer cells that line the tissue…and in situ classifies the type of cells in the area as either low, intermediate, or high grade…*[1]

1. Memorial Sloan Kettering Cancer Center, *Types of Breast Cancer*, n.d., https://www. mskcc.org/cancer-care/types/breast/types-breast?amp&pn_mapping=pn_11&gcli-d=Cj0KCQiAmeKQBhDvARIsAHJ7mF71XDrJP-FSpk-dSoA31cLSTl6GglfbLxtffiB-cz_nvJJnaZMS7SR4aAi8EEALw_wcB.

Perhaps hearing my silence and sensing my shock, my doctor moved forward to address the positive aspect of my case: the cancer appeared to be contained within one area, rather than having spread into other local parts such as the lymph nodes.

There was also a lot, I would learn later, that she chose not to disclose in that moment, such as how TNBC is more difficult to treat because it does not respond to drugs that target estrogen, progesterone, or HER2 receptors;[2] how this cancer has a higher return rate than any other type of breast cancer; how triple negative breast cancer tends to grow and spread faster; how there is a 12% survival rate if not detected early.[3]

In short, TNBC was considered a death sentence.

Still, *not* knowing any of this, I melted into my husband's arms and tears began to pour uncontrollably down my face. Brian turned the phone off speaker mode and finished the call for me, because I couldn't breathe let alone speak. As I continued to cry, he wrapped his arms tightly around me and gently kissed the top of my head. I didn't want to move from that position. I wanted to stay in the comfort of his embrace forever and pretend none of this had ever happened.

---

2. Ibid.

3. American Cancer Society, *Triple Negative Breast Cancer*, 2021, https://www.cancer.org/cancer/breast-cancer/about/types-of-breast-cancer/triple-negative.html.

My mind was racing and projecting all possible outcomes, most of which were not positive. In between sobs, the only word that could escape my mouth was the word I dreaded most: chemo.

I was petrified of that word. I could accept the outcome of needing surgery; that was a familiar road to me having gone down it with my mom, but I could not quite wrap my head around the possibility of needing chemo. Chemotherapy was such an unknown territory and I had heard nothing but horror stories about it.

I also couldn't help playing that dangerous hypothetical mind game: *what if* my body rejects the treatments or *what if* the chemo makes me feel physically ill. I also thought *what if* I lose my hair, however that was the least of my worries at that time, as I was primarily focused on the condition of my health.

While my head was pressed against my husband's chest, and I was drowning in my tears and fears, Brian quietly spoke wise and comforting words to me. He explained how we should not assume that I would need chemo; instead, he suggested we should focus on one day at a time while keeping our sights on getting through my surgery. His words calmed my heart and reminded me of all the ways God had already been by my side through the process thus far, strategically guiding my every step; and in that moment, I felt sure He would continue to do so.

"I will never leave you nor forsake you,"[4] flashed into my mind, one of God's greatest promises.

My heart clenched upon that promise, and I finally lifted my head and looked up into my husband's eyes. He kissed my tear-stained cheeks and walked me over to the couch, where we sat down, and I was finally able to catch my breath.

Once I was able to construct an intelligible sentence, we discussed a plan of action: we would contact our friend for advice on a breast surgeon, fly back to New Jersey to meet with the surgeon and have the surgery there. However, we did not account for God's plan. Minutes after we spoke with our friend, a hospital coordinator called and asked if I was available to meet with the surgeon the following day at noon. I hung up the phone and we booked our tickets for the 6:00am flight to New Jersey on the following day.

The next few days were a blur, but I could not ignore how everything seemed to fall perfectly into place, which brought more peace to my heart. I know it is odd to describe any part of my cancer journey with the word peace, but it was true. In the early days of my diagnosis, I could tangibly feel God's hand on my life, as though there was a strange order amidst all the chaos. Ever since the phone call from the insurance representative, the entire process had an indescribable and effortless flow to it, as if God had been clearing all the doctor's

---

4. Deuteronomy 31:6. NIV.

calendars and scheduling all the appointments on my behalf. The only thing He asked of me was that I trust Him.

While I was a woman of strong faith and found joy in teaching others about the power of trusting God, I found myself at a pivotal juncture in my faith: was I going to practice what I preached?

# CHAPTER

# TWO

From the moment of my diagnosis, I knew I wanted to have a bilateral mastectomy. Even though there were other options available, I decided that was the best course of action for me, as I am a proactive person and wanted to take all measures possible to reduce the risk of my cancer returning.

My decisiveness about the situation made our conversation with the surgeon productive and efficient, as we were able to discuss this topic in depth and have all our questions answered. The doctor was confident in my decision and my trust in her surgery skills was reciprocated, as she had operated on my mother. Brian and I left her office with a tentative surgery date on the calendar and an appointment with a recommended plastic surgeon for the reconstruction (the same doctor who performed my mother's procedure).

It was a busy yet productive Friday morning, straight from the airport to the doctor's office then to my parent's home, but I was happy to be moving forward. Having a solid plan in place allowed me to relax and enjoy time with my family during the next two weeks leading up to my surgery, and for once, place the cancer card slightly towards the back of my mind. I appreciated the ways in which my family tried their best to resume normal activities and conversations and steer clear of the dialogue surrounding my diagnosis.

During that two-week period, I focused on doing things that made me happy: doing my regular workouts, maintaining excellent nutrition and a healthy diet, spending time with family and friends, and frequenting salon chairs for my feel-good blowouts.

Feeling good in that chair, however, was proving difficult. As I sat down in the salon chair and swiveled around to glance at my reflection in the mirror, the reality of my breast cancer diagnosis hit.

Suddenly, as I stared at my reflection, I did not feel invincible, beautiful, glamorous, or confident - I felt numb. The once comforting rhythmic pull of the round brush and warm heat of the hair dryer against my head felt distant. My body was present and enjoying the relaxing spa experience, but my mind was worlds away: fixated on the fact that I had cancer. The dreaded six-letter-word that seemed almost impossible for a healthy, athletic, thirty-eight-year-old woman like me.

I continued to stare at my reflection in the mirror and tried my best to resist the tears from welling up within my eyes. Despite successfully fighting them back, I began to realize that the negative power from my thoughts had already started to impact the physiology of my body, and my breathing pattern was quickly escalating in pace.

In addition to all my mixed emotions, I was confused on how I was allowing myself to be in such a mentally and spiritually weakened state. I kept thinking how it was so unlike me and repetitively asked myself "What is happening to me?" Grateful for a bottle of water in my hand, I closed my eyes and took a long sip to calm myself.

My fast-paced breathing pattern had not dissipated by the time I had opened my eyes. Additionally, the more I observed the busy atmosphere and friendly chatter amongst clients and beauticians, the more the walls of the salon gradually began to inch their way closer to my chair. Feeling trapped, I started to sweat, my face turned bright red, and I could feel the heat penetrating through the surface of my skin. My stylist took note of the change in my demeanor and asked if I was alright. I lied and said I was fine.

I realized I was experiencing my first panic attack, and immediately thought that I should excuse myself and go to the bathroom. However, the idea of being in a small, closed room, alone, with the door locked was causing me to feel faint, so I remained seated in the chair and focused on breathing, drinking my water, telling myself that my mom would soon arrive to pick me up, and praying to God.

However, that moment of prayer in the salon chair felt different, because it was the first time, I experienced my faith being tested; the first time God felt distant. He no longer seemed like the friend who was by my side through thick and thin; rather, the friend who I kept frantically trying to get in touch with and wound up with their voicemail every time.

It was the first time, too, the dark, fearful thought that God had abandoned me and didn't care about me crossed my mind. I tried to snap myself back to reality by recalling one of God's greatest promises from Deuteronomy 31:6: He will *never* leave me or forsake me. I remembered the message behind all my journal entries: God is working even when we can't see His Work or understand it; and when life seems as though it is spiraling out of control, He is still working on our behalf.

And yet, as I rose from the chair and took a long, hard stare at my reflection in the mirror – intact on the outside yet, broken down on the inside - I couldn't help but think about the goodness of God and all the miraculous ways in which He had already intervened in my life.

I paid for my blowout and stepped outside into the summer heat. Relieved to be outside in the open air, my breathing calmed, and I reminded myself of the true meaning of having faith: unwavering *trust* and *hope* in God; that I must *trust* that He is with me even when I can't see Him; that I must also *trust* that He has a good plan for my life and *hope* I will be alright. This was the *faith* I had chosen to guide my life, regardless of the obstacles I'd endured, and regardless of those that would soon come.

Shifting one's perspective from pain into praise or frustration into faith, however, is often easier said than done. It is not always easy to *keep the faith*, and I continued to experience that struggle.

While the panic attacks subsided, I soon became petrified to eat. It is a weird thing knowing you have a cancer tumor growing inside of you, and it is even stranger having no idea how you contracted it. Every time I ate something I thought to myself: "is this making my cancer worse?"

I consulted my nutritionist for advice, so I could stop mentally tormenting myself. We communicated everyday via text or email about my food journals to make sure I obtained proper amounts of protein, healthy carbohydrates, vegetables, greens, and more vegetables and greens.

Eating right provided encouragement and confidence for the days ahead - except for one small lingering thought in the back of my mind, which rose to the surface one night as I lay in bed:

"What happens if I die?"

So, I did what I always do: I talked to Jesus about it, verbalizing out loud all my thoughts and concerns to Him.

It was through these personal conversations when I realized that the more I talked out loud to Jesus, the more my mind began to transform and renew. All previous, negative thoughts began to dissipate and be replaced with gratitude towards God and all the incredible ways He was working in my life.

I rolled over in bed and reached for my journal and pen on the nightstand and once again put my thoughts into action by writing down three things I was grateful for. I thanked God for His strong Presence in my life, His intentionality of interceding at exactly the right moment, and His ability to bring goodness out of any negative situation.

Immediately, I felt calmed and positive, and an unsurmountable peace came over my heart. I was also reminded that the more I focused on gratitude and my relationship with God the clearer I was in hearing His voice. The way I had become familiar with God's voice and all the ways He speaks had been the same way I got to know any other person: by spending time with them.

I had found that while spending time with a person, I not only learn their voice, but learn about their character, talents, and personality. I had also found that the same held true for getting to know God. When I'd taken time to be alone with Him, talk to Him, and read about Him (in the Bible), I'd begun to understand who He is. If I wanted to continue to be more in-tune to His voice and the ways He was speaking to me, then I needed to consistently spend more time with Him.

I continued my conversations the remainder of that week prior to surgery, during which I had to quarantine, as the newly detected Delta variant of COVID-19 was surging throughout the United States. Many of our friends in Florida were testing positive, as well as family and friends in New Jersey. Even though I had already contracted the original strand of COVID-19 in 2020 and had since been double vaccinated, I was committed to follow all necessary precautions, including self-isolating.

I was on high alert to remain healthy and not get sick, which meant my husband and parents had to make the same efforts as me. They not only followed all the recommended precautions but also limited their visits to stores, restaurants, and seeing people outside of their direct work circle.

It was a Monday afternoon when Brian entered through

the back door of my parents' house with grocery bags in hand. He had just finished a productive day in the office and picked up dinner for us on the way home. With all our company employees working from home, due to the pandemic, it was nice that we did not have to worry about him coming in direct contact with anyone sick at the office.

As we were unloading the groceries, I asked him about his day, and he shared details with me including one conversation that caught my attention. He said that he had spoken to his son, who also works for our company, and proceeded to tell me that the two of them would be meeting in the office later in the week to record some industry related videos in the office studio. As I set down a bundle of bananas, I felt something inside that was a cross between a whisper and nudge.

I didn't exactly know why the idea of Brian meeting his son in the office wasn't settling right with me, but it wasn't, and, as the whisper from the Holy Spirit from deep inside of me continued, I stopped unbagging groceries and turned towards Brian.

"I don't think it is a good idea for you to see him this week," I said.

He tilted his head and squinted with a look that didn't need a verbal explanation. I could practically read his thoughts: *Don't you think you are being a little extreme with the*

*COVID measures?*

I felt somewhat guilty with the words I spoke next, because, of course, I wanted him to see his son. Besides that, I had no real logic behind my request for him to not to.

"I'm sorry...*I just have this feeling* that it is not the best thing to do," I said. Then, as if my thoughts, words, and feelings were a mixed bag of prayers going right up to God's ears, the Holy Spirit's voice inside of me grew clearer, and provided me with reason to be precautious. "Also..." I asked Brian: "Isn't your son traveling?" Brian confirmed that his son was away in Florida and would be returning in two days. I didn't have to say much more, as Brian understood my concern and agreed that it would be best to wait until the following week to see his son.

Three days later, Brian's son tested positive for COVID. After Brian told me the news, I distinctly remember sitting on my parent's couch praying for his son's complete healing and praising God for His hand of protection over my life. I could not stop thanking God for speaking to me that day in the kitchen.

# CHAPTER
# THREE

My iPhone alarm sounded at 6:00am on Monday, August 23, 2021. I lifted my eye mask and reached over to the bedside table to silence the beeping device, and caught a glimpse of the electronic, guest room telephone out of the corner of my eye. The old school desk phone with a blinking red light, indicating a voice message needed to be retrieved, reminded me that I was not in my own bed.

I stared at the phone a moment longer, in a sleepy and confused state, until my eyes drifted a few inches to the side and observed the small pad, pen, and in-room dining menu. I flipped off the covers, woke up Brian, and woke up my parents who were sleeping in the adjoining room. It was time to shower, get dressed, and head to the surgery center.

We were staying at The MC Hotel in Montclair, New Jersey, just eight miles from the location of my procedure. Since my operation was slotted for 8:00am, and my parents' house was an hour away, we thought it was best to stay at a local hotel. This would eliminate the stress of getting up early and potentially hitting rush hour traffic. Also, since my double mastectomy was now considered a "day stay" operation, due to COVID precautions, we opted to spend an additional night at the hotel, which gave me comfort knowing my doctors were close by should I require any medical attention.

Brian plugged the destination into Google Maps and rallied our smiles by energetically shouting one of his signature phrases: "Here we go team!" He'd used the phrase for past adventures, like exploring cities and towns in Europe, but his humor worked and brought a smile to my face.

Aside from Brian's clever conversational ice breaker, no one really knew what to say next. The silence became palpable, and I braced myself for the awkward twenty-minute car ride ahead. It didn't help knowing that the COVID precautions were still heavily enforced throughout the state of New Jersey, which meant no one would be able to accompany me inside the building. While we understood the purpose behind the protocol, it added unnecessary stress to an already stressful situation.

Determined to keep my spirits high, I grabbed my phone, turned on my favorite worship play list, and sat back to relax as the music played. However, about ten minutes into the ride, my state of relaxation was quietly interrupted when I could overhear my mother crying from the backseat. I assumed it was a combination of the words from the music and her maternal emotions of worry and protection for her daughter. A piece of me sympathized with her and understood her perspective, yet, in that moment, I knew I couldn't allow myself to become impacted by her feelings. It was imperative that I remained positive and posture my perspective on the One who was in complete control. So, I turned the volume up and without holding back, I started to sing and worship.

As I did, a part of me felt ready and completely at peace with stepping into my surgery; at the same time, because of this peaceful feeling, there was another part of me that hoped the car ride wouldn't end.

We arrived at the surgery center, and it struck me as odd having to hug my family in the parking lot and say good-bye. *Was it good-bye?*

After Brian and I hugged, kissed, and snapped a quick selfie together, he squeezed my hand one last time and I walked towards the entrance of the building. As I approached the automatic, sliding, glass doors, I stopped, inhaled a breath of fresh air and said:

"Here we go Jesus."

As I took a step forward, the motion detector signaled the sliding doors to open, and as if in answer to my call, Jesus seemed to shroud me with His presence and become my private bodyguard to escort and comfort me every step of the way. I started at the registration desk, then moved to the changing area where I needed to put on a hospital gown, stowed away my personal belongings, and then we took about a half-hour pit stop at a pre-op station.

With the sterile blue, cotton curtains pulled around on all four sides of the gurney bed, nurses tended to me in a quick and efficient manner; each owning a specific responsibility: check my vital signs, insert my intravenous tube, review my medical chart, confirm my surgery details, and educate me on the anesthesia and recovery process. Everything moved forward at a brisk, effortless pace, and I continued to feel Jesus's love towards me radiating through every employee's kind words and gentle touch. I felt comfortable and confident that I was in the right place and in the right hands.

After all the boxes had been checked, I sat patiently on the gurney waiting for my doctors to come consult with me before heading into the operating room. Sitting there while waiting and continuing to feel God's presence, I began to notice the plainness of my appearance.

I glanced at the IV in my left arm, then gazed down to the trendy, red, non-slip, hospital socks covering my feet, and proceeded to study the light blue, neutral print of my hospital gown. I found that the longer I stared at the pattern, the more I experienced an overwhelming emotion of nakedness. Even though I was not technically naked, I felt stripped and vulnerable.

I observed my hands without rings, my nails without polish, my wrists without bracelets, my body without clothes, my ears without earrings, and shoulders without a designer handbag adorning them, and I couldn't help but to silently ask Jesus: *Is this how it will be when I go to heaven?* But He didn't need to respond, I knew the answer.

All those *things* would not accompany me to heaven. They are just that: *things.* They are temporary, earthly things, and even though they made me feel pretty on the outside, I knew they didn't define the inner beauty. I knew, too, that although I enjoyed material things, but that they were not really my joy. They were a piece of my love language, but they were not where my love resided.

That moment was a sharp reminder that while it was good to enjoy the blessings in this earthly life, I must never allow myself to seek fulfillment or purpose within them. My true identity can only be found within God. Feeling more secure in my natural, raw state, I smiled and thanked God for that much-needed reality check.

Moments later, my surgeon and her assistant arrived to review everything with me. They were the perfect combination of kind and confident, making it possible for me to relax and feel confident that I was in excellent hands.

I was told my surgery would last for three hours. Half would be delegated for my surgeon to remove all the breast tissue, cancerous tumor, and one sentinel lymph node to test and make sure the cancer had not spread. The other half would be delegated for my plastic surgeon to begin the reconstructive process by inserting temporary breast expanders.

My surgeon told me she would call my husband from the operating room after her portion of the surgery was over to update him on my status. She also said that she would expedite the testing process of my lymph node, so that she would have the results back before calling my husband. She assured me that I would do great, said my plastic surgeon was on his way to see me, and that she would see me shortly in the operating room.

As I thanked her and her team for taking such good care of me, my heart smiled, and my eyes started to well with tears of gratitude towards God. I could feel all the ways He was working all around me to make this experience as comfortable as possible, as every detail seemed curated with care.

It wasn't long before my plastic surgeon's assistant arrived greeting me with a giant smile and a warm sisterly embrace. Since both she and my plastic surgeon had provided me with their cell phone numbers the few weeks prior to surgery, enabling me to reach out with any question, we had become good friends.

We talked for a few minutes, when I heard my plastic surgeon approaching - I recognized the distinct, clomping sound of his wooden clogs hitting the floor as they neared my station. A moment later, the curtain in front of me swung open and my plastic surgeon entered with a warm smile on his face.

He asked how I was doing, sat down in the chair next to my gurney, and had me stand up straight to mark my chest with a lovely, blue, surgical, sharpie marker, which I would later learn took some serious scrubbing to remove. As he was marking me, we chatted while his assistant bounced in and out of the room to make sure everything was being properly prepared, and I felt a specific familial comfort reside within me. The type of comfort and contentment I felt when sitting on a couch in warm sweats and wrapped in a soft blanket amongst close family and friends.

Whether they knew it or not, the gesture of allowing me to text them anytime during the previous weeks, made me feel like they knew and understood me better than if we had just talked on the day of consult and surgery. They had become an intricate part of my journey and were like family to me, and their incredible positivity and enthusiastic energy felt contagious. "You're going to do amazing!" they kept saying, which made me feel confidant and even excited for my surgery to begin.

With the best medical team and God by my side, what could possibly go wrong?

The clock ticked 8:32am and the nurse informed me that it was time for me to be wheeled into the operating room. She positioned herself behind me, unlocked the wheel breaks of my gurney, and slowly began to push me across the pre-operative waiting room. We then journeyed through a wide set of metal-framed, automatic doors which led into a large hallway and continued forward until we reached my assigned room.

The views from the gurney were pleasant enough as I passed by other patients waiting their turn to go into surgery, doctors dressed in their teal green scrubs consulting with them, and the bustling nurse's station. However, as I passed by all the medical equipment, episodes from the television show *Grey's Anatomy* flashed into my mind, and I couldn't help but remember all the stressful operating room scenes I had watched. I started to become a little apprehensive thinking I would experience another panic attack while going into the room, but just as we entered the room, a team of physician assistants (PAs) were there waiting for my arrival. They greeted me by name and came over to help me move from my gurney onto the operating table, which left me no time to think of anything else but taking my next step. All previous feelings of apprehension had dissipated.

With the IV still attached to my arm, I slowly made my way to the operating table, gradually laid back while staring up at the large, white, lights hanging above my body and admired the accuracy of *Grey's Anatomy* production sets.

The PAs and anesthesiologist attended to me by strapping down my arms in a "T" position. A woman at my feet draped warm blankets over my feet and legs, and strapped a transparent, rubber face mask over my nose and mouth. Then, the anesthesiologist asked me where my favorite place in the world was.

I opened my mouth to say Montalcino, Italy.

Then I was out.

# CHAPTER
# FOUR

Three and a half hours later, I awoke in an upright, seated position of a gurney chair. I looked around and immediately recognized the long, cotton, curtains surrounding me on all four sides, but then noted two distinct differences from my previous pre-op location. The nurse's station was now positioned directly in front of me, and there seemed to be a new mellow and quiet atmosphere to the room. I was struggling to figure out my exact location, when suddenly, my specific whereabouts became completely irrelevant, and I remembered that my surgery must have been over. I gasped excitedly and said to myself: "I did it! Thank you, Jesus!"

Without another thought, I looked down and saw the

familiar blue, floral print brace, the same kind that my mother wore, wrapped tightly around my chest. Safety pinned to the front of the brace were four, clear tubes that were attached to the sides of my body and actively draining excess blood and breast tissue into the grenade-shaped drains that hung from the bottom of the tubes.

A nurse spotted my alertness through an open slit in the curtain and came walking over. She asked how I was feeling and explained that I could remain there, in the post-operative waiting room, until I felt ready to leave. I thanked her for taking care of me, and without hesitation, preceded to ask if my lymph nodes were clear. She confirmed that the cancer had not spread to them, and I sighed with relief upon hearing this great news and thought how happy my family must have been to receive that call from my surgeon while I was in the operating room.

The nurse then opened a small can of apple juice and a bag of graham crackers, and my stomach started to growl at the sight of the food. I didn't realize how hungry I was and consumed the bite-sized crackers and juice within seconds. Two bags of crackers and two cans of juice later, I slowly started to stand up from the chair and get dressed, while avoiding any large movements with my arms.

After I returned to my chair, the nurse reviewed the discharge instructions, confirmed my one-week follow up appointment with my plastic surgeon, and handed me a goodie bag containing a plastic measuring cup and a few photocopies of a form to record my daily routine. She informed me that I would need to empty each drain twice a day, morning and night, into the measuring cup and record the amount of liquid emptied on the forms. I nodded my head in comprehension, as I was well aware of this tedious protocol from my previous experience of assisting my mother with her drains.

It was around 2:30pm when the nurse assisted me into a wheelchair and transported me outside to meet my family. Brian had the car pulled around to the front entrance of the building and the three of them were standing outside wearing joyous smiles on their faces.

As my wheelchair ride came to a stop, the nurse handed Brian my goodie bag, along with my other personal belongings, and then each of them stood on either side to assist me out of the chair. However, with sutures underneath my breasts and in my right armpit (where the lymph node was removed), I was unable to put any weight or pressure on my arms. I had to pause for a moment and become extremely intentional about every movement I made.

With Brian on one side of me and the nurse on the other, I placed one hand in his and the other in the nurse's hand to balance myself, planted my feet firmly on the ground, and slowly lifted myself out of the chair using the strength from my legs and core. Brian continued by my side as I walked to the car door where he helped me slide into the front seat. After I was comfortably seated, he slid a small pillow between the seatbelt and my chest, a little comfort trick my mom told me about, and closed the passenger door. When everyone was situated in their seats, we started our trip back to the hotel.

I spent the remainder of the day relaxing in bed with dozens of pillows propped up around me, as using my hands or arms for leverage to help me up was not an option. When dinner time came around, my mother made me my go-to, non-alcoholic beverage, club soda with a splash of cranberry juice, and we used DoorDash to order food from a local Italian restaurant.

After Brian and I finished eating dinner at the little table for two in the corner of our room, I went into the bathroom to conduct my nightly skincare regiment in attempt to normalize – and also because I had always had a slight obsession with skincare, never skipping my morning or night face routine.

As I turned on the bathroom light and looked in the mirror, I immediately noticed the bright orange iodine stains on my skin from the doctors which covered my upper chest, parts of my shoulders, and the base of my neck. I noticed, too, the extreme flatness and formless shape of my chest, along with the prominent, red-filled tubes and drains affixed to the front of my brace. My reflection was definitely my least glamorous look ever, but I was grateful at least for my intact blowout.

I cleansed, toned, moisturized, while adding a little serum, hydrating oil, and eye cream into the mix, sprayed my hair with a touch of my favorite dry shampoo product, Kevin Murphy DOO.OVER, hoping to get another day out of my hair, hit the light switch off, and shuffled my way towards bed.

As Brian helped to prop the pillows on my bed and guide me into a comfortable sleeping position, my plastic surgeon's PA called to check in and see how I was doing. I told her how I was expecting to be in pain or discomfort, but aside from the pressure around my chest from the brace, I was not experiencing any real discomfort or other adverse side effects. She was happy to hear that I was doing well and reminded me to stay on top of my drains, and of course, to text or call her any time with questions.

I fell asleep that night in complete peace and with a smile on my face, as I felt God's hedge of protection around my life. I was so grateful that He had intervened in my life with perfect timing; to show me the cancer within my body that I never would have discovered on my own. I was also beyond grateful for all the wonderful doctors He brought into my life to successfully remove it, and I was forever grateful for a successful surgery without complications, and a strong, healthy body that could endure an invasive double mastectomy.

Although I was lying in bed in a weakened physical state, my spirits were strong. I could feel God and His angels working around the clock on my behalf, eliminating pieces of the journey they knew I could not endure and joining and strengthening me during the hard times in which I was fighting. That night at the hotel, with the blue brace wrapped tightly around my chest, four drains securely fastened, and pillows piled high, I had one of the best nights of sleep I ever had.

I awoke to Brian's gentle touch and soft words saying that it was time to get ready and head back home. I strategically swiveled my legs over the side of the bed, carefully stood up, and went through the motions of my morning routine while constantly reminding myself not to lift my arms above a ninety-degree angle.

Eventually, we made our way down to the hotel lobby where Brian and my parents packed up the car and helped me into the front seat. When we were all buckled in, Brian grabbed his phone, entered our destination into Google Maps, and pulled out of the hotel entrance energetically announcing again: "here we go team!" Of course, I couldn't help but smile and think about how grateful I was to have him as my husband, by far the greatest blessing in my life.

Avoiding potholes and sharp turns, Brian safely chauffeured us into my parents' driveway. I walked inside, soaking up the comfort of their home, and went to the special, lift recliner chair we had rented from a local pharmacy for the few weeks of my recovery. A piece of me did feel bad for completely neglecting my favorite, leather, club chair and ottoman looking empty and lonely and staring at me from across the living room, although I felt as though I had made a serious upgrade. Not only could this La-Z-Boy chair adjust to a flat, horizontal position, it could tilt forward to allow me to easily slide out of the chair without using my arms. Whoever invented that chair is brilliant.

Little did I know that this chair would not only become my workstation, Netflix cinema seat, and bed for the next four weeks, but also the place where a personal transformation would initiate.

# CHAPTER
# FIVE

A s the first week of post-surgery glided by, I was amazed at how I was experiencing *zero* pain after such an intense surgery, and that I only had to take Tylenol for a few random headaches. I was becoming more eager with each new day to get my drains removed, as they were awkward, tedious, and cumbersome. However, with all the positivity around me, it was difficult not to feel a sense of extreme peace during the entire experience thus far, as it was clear that God was continually providing for me through this storm.

Add to this the incredible support I was receiving. Over the next few weeks, my parents' house seemed transformed into a chic flower and gift boutique. The abundant amount of love that poured through the front door - stunning floral bouquets, sentimental cards, and incredibly thoughtful get-well gifts - was overwhelmingly beautiful. That didn't even include all the Facebook and Instagram messages, emails, text messages, and phone calls I received. I was extremely touched knowing how much both my personal friends and business colleagues from around the world were thinking and praying for me, and I cried upon hearing the news of how one of my husband's friends who leads a church in Budaka, Uganda was holding a vigil in my name. Prayer is so powerful, and I felt a palpable, circle of love surrounding my life.

In addition to every heartfelt prayer that went up before God's presence on my behalf, there was one specific prayer that altered my life.

It was a quiet morning in my parents' home. My father and Brian were at work, and my mother was home tending to me. I had just finished my quiet time, which consisted of prayer and Bible and devotional passage reading, when I made my way towards the bathroom to shower and get ready for another day of lounging around the house.

As I turned around to close the bathroom door, the cell phone in my hand rang. I looked down and saw that it was one of my and Brian's dear friends, who happened to be a pastor at a church in Summit, New Jersey. I answered the phone, and my friend said how he was so happy to hear the upbeat tone of my voice. He asked how I was feeling physically, and I told him I was feeling great and updated him with details about the days leading up until that point. He then asked how my spiritual health had been since the day of my diagnosis, knowing that spiritual health is critical in moments such as this. I explained that even though the past few weeks had been a whirlwind of events, I truly felt blessed by all the ways God was moving in life.

My friend was very encouraged by my optimism and prior to ending our conversation, he asked if he could pray for me. I emphatically responded: "Of course. I would love that." He asked if there was something specific I would like him to pray for, and I requested a healthy and quick healing process and to remain cancer free.

My friend said he would absolutely pray for those things and asked if he could add something else to the prayer as well. I said: "Absolutely," and walked over and sat down on top of the toilet seat cover and closed my eyes while holding the phone to my ear with one hand and the other on my lap with my palm facing the ceiling, in a receiving position.

My friend prayed for complete healing over me, and I felt relaxed and calm listening to his words. However, towards the end of his prayer, the theme of his prayer started to take a drastic turn, as I heard him say: "I pray that Carrie would be *teachable* during this chapter of her life."

My eyes shot open at the sound of that word 'teachable' and

I thought to myself: *What was he talking about?*

Without knowing my reaction, my friend's words continued to flow, and he prayed that I would become open and *teachable* to see and understand all the lessons in which God was trying to reveal to me. He recognized this was a difficult season for me but believed that there were lessons I could glean from it that may not be obtainable through any other period in my life.

As his prayer ended, we both said a heartfelt: "Amen," and I thanked him so much for calling and taking the time to pray for me. However, after I tapped the red "end call" button of my iPhone, I remained seated on top of the toilet seat for a few moments longer digesting the meaning of his prayer.

I had expected him to pray a sympathetic prayer of some sort, not a curveball prayer that would challenge me.

Understanding that God may be trying to speak to me through my friend's words, I decided right there to accept the challenge.

I stood up and walked out of the bathroom towards my chair repeating to myself: *Teachable. Teachable. God what you are trying to teach me?*

With my type-A, immediate gratification personality, I wanted to instantaneously know all the lessons God was trying to teach me. I didn't want to wait. Patience and waiting were not my forte, let alone part of my regular vocabulary.

I wanted my Teacher to teach me now, so that I could be a good student and implement everything I had learned. But then I remembered that my plans are not always God's plans. In fact, my plans are often short-sighted and small compared to God's elaborate and great plans for my life: to prosper me and give me hope and a great future.[5]

With my future resting in God's hands and seeming brighter than ever, I began to recall some of my favorite scriptural promises, and flipped to the ear-marked pages of my Bible where these love notes from God were highlighted in neon yellow:

*"Be strong and courageous... for the Lord your God goes with you; he will never leave you nor forsake you." – Deuteronomy 31:6*

*"The steadfast love of the Lord never ceases; his mercies never come to an end; they are new every morning" – Lamentations 3:22-23*

"Do not be anxious about anything, but in every situation, by prayer and petition, with thanksgiving, present your requests to God. And the peace of God, which transcends all understanding, will guard your hearts and your minds in

---

5. Jeremiah 29:11. NIV.

Christ Jesus." – Philippians 4:6-7

"Be still, and know that I am God; I will be exalted among the nations, I will be exalted in the earth." – Psalm 46:10

With every verse I read, I felt secure in my new waiting period. Whether that would be days, weeks, months, or years, I didn't know, but my faith in God was becoming more firmly established. I knew that waiting periods require patience; it was a message I often preached, and now I was being tested to exemplify it. I was being Called to live by my faith: to trust in Him, depend on Him, and know every lesson will be revealed in His perfect timing.

With that thought, I turned to the promise of Proverbs 3:

*"Trust in the Lord with all your heart; do not depend on your own understanding. Seek His will in all you do, and He will show you which path to take."*

The truth behind that verse produced a great confidence within me knowing that God would show me the way. In the meantime, there was only one thing He was requesting of me, and I wrote it down in my Bible: remain *teachable*.

In the days that followed that call, I became more invigorated and motivated to seek God and discover the underlying significance of this season of life. I routinely asked myself questions such as: *How can I grow through this cancer experience? How can I serve God and His people throughout this period?*

One morning, while Brian and my father were at work and my mother was in the other room working out, I lounged back in the recliner and started talking to Jesus as if He were sitting across from me in the leather club chair. I dissected my entire journey to Him, starting from the insurance phone call leading right up to my current position in the recliner lift chair, thanking Him for all the incredible miracles He had performed along the way. Even though He already knew everything I was telling Him, it felt good to talk to Him about it all.

Suddenly, as I was talking out loud, reminiscing, and professing my complete awe in how He knows every intricate detail of my life, it occurred to me that I had just learned my first lesson. Through my simple conversation with God, I realized that gratitude was the ideal gateway to posture my heart for receiving more of God's wisdom.

I grabbed my journal from the coffee table next to me, turned to a blank page, and once again wrote down three things I was grateful for within the last twenty-four hours.

1. I am so grateful that I am healing well and without any pain.

2. I am so grateful for my dear friend who prayed over me and sparked a new challenge of obedience within my heart.

3. I am so grateful for my loving husband and parents who are taking such good care of me.

It was in that moment of reflection where I decided that I would not allow the word 'cancer,' or the temporary, uncomfortable tissue expanders planted in my chest, or the ugly image of the drains bring me down. My mind would not be occupied by my circumstances, instead, it would remain focused on shaping, molding, and creating my personal testimony to share with others.

There was so much goodness happening around me, and although some days were easier than others to seek the positive, I knew that if I kept my heart and mind rooted in my faith, then I could only produce good character, lessons, and stories.

# CHAPTER
# SIX

The three weeks post-surgery had a systematic flow to them, consisting mostly of my routinely emptying the drains, taking brisk walks outside, maintaining a high protein diet (imperative for the healing process), carving out daily quiet time with God, journaling, getting blowouts by my mother in the living room chair, and visiting my plastic surgeon.

The weekly trips to his office were so he could adjust the expanders and evaluate the drains. During my first appointment, I tried to negotiate a way to have him remove all the drains. Unfortunately, my negotiation skills proved unsuccessful, as my doctor explained that it was critical to allot enough time for the new blood flow to be established, and ultimately, prevent a clot from forming. I understood his defensive argument and was happy to settle when he offered to remove one of the four. I was ecstatic at his proposal and walked out of the office with one less drain stitched into my side.

As I continued to observe all the proper recovery protocols, the next step was to schedule an appointment with an oncologist who would discuss any further treatment recommendations, which I secretly dreaded.

With my parents' house only an hour from New York City, I decided that it would be best to research oncologists at Memorial Sloan Kettering Hospital (MSK) that specialize in triple negative breast cancer, in addition to an oncologist through the hospital where I had my surgery, Cooperman Barnabas Medical Center, as my family agreed it was imperative to have at least two opinions be part of the treatment process. However, the idea of calling doctors' offices, remaining on hold for an indefinite amount of time, and faxing my records, was not appealing to me. Simply thinking about that entire process was exhausting, and as a result, I became a little reluctant in initiating the process. Additionally, I did not want to put any further stress on myself in the early stages of my recovery.

I waited until my next appointment with my plastic surgeon to ask him if there was an oncologist that he recommended. He willingly gave me the name and number to a great doctor, who I was able to book an appointment with, so I immediately started to feel at ease.

While I was feeling encouraged to be making some sort of progress in the appointment department, a piece of me still wanted to secure something with an oncologist at MSK. My family's advice suddenly seemed important to me, and I'd started to agree that a second opinion was important but did not know where to start. Confirming an appointment with a doctor at one of the most famous hospitals in the world seemed daunting, impossible, and exhausting all rolled into one.

Then, one distinct evening where my mother was cooking dinner, Brian was working on his computer, my father was reading the newspaper, and I had relocated to the couch for a few hours, something incredible happened. I was catching up on social media posts and responding to people's kind messages and comments, when a certain direct message caught my attention. It was from one my Gamma Phi Beta sorority sisters from Gettysburg College who I had not talked to in at least fifteen years.

With my curiosity sparked, I opened the message and saw a very long text bubble. Scrolling through the message,

I read how she was following my posts on Facebook and was so sorry to hear about my recent diagnosis. Then, she continued by sharing a piece of her story that I did not know: her mother had recently been diagnosed with triple negative breast cancer and she was deeply involved in tending to her mother's physical and emotional needs. Her story struck a chord in my heart, and my eyes welled up with tears thinking about the similar road they were walking down. I could relate with her on so many levels and sympathized with her struggles.

I continued to scroll downward in the message, and she preceded to say that in addition to helping her mother navigate the daily, unknown territory of cancer, she had also taken on the responsibility of researching different oncologists at MSK. She included names and phone numbers of some of the top triple negative breast cancer oncologists at MSK who came highly recommend to her and concluded by saying that she hoped this information was helpful and to reach out at any time.

Now the tears were really starting to flow down my cheeks. I don't think my sorority sister knew it, but her message was not only a wealth of information, providing me with the oncologist that I would eventually meet with, but it was an answer to prayer.

I recounted the entire story to Brian and we agreed that

God was, yet again, paving the way for me, and that I should reach out to the recommended oncologist the following day to schedule an appointment.

I figured that it would be best to call first thing in the morning before the phone lines got busy. I set an alarm for 9:00am and dialed the doctor's number hoping to secure an appointment within the next few days. I knew that was somewhat wishful thinking since she was one of the leading oncologists in the country for triple negative breast cancer research, but I also knew that nothing is impossible with God.

After a solid hour of working to get my information registered into the MSK system, I was told that my request to see the doctor would be submitted and her office would call me if my request was approved. I had not anticipated that response and felt a little roadblock trying to hedge between me and my plan.

I hung up the phone and pulled up my text message app, opening to a previous conversation with one of my dear friends and longtime doctor at New York Presbyterian - Weill Cornell Medical Center, and thought to myself: *It can't hurt to ask.*

I started to type a message asking my friend if he knew the oncologist I wanted to see, and if so, would he be willing to write her a recommendation on my behalf. He responded within minutes stating that he knew her and would be happy to send her a note. The doctor's office reached out within forty-eight hours to schedule an appointment. I was overjoyed and added this event as another journal entry to my long list of blessings.

Week three rolled around, and I was finally freed from the four, rubber chains hanging from my body, as the drains were removed: a major highlight in my gratitude journal. My doctor was happy with my healing progress, and I was happy that I could start wearing normal tops again.

Prior to being drain free, my wardrobe selections had consisted of two main options: (1) custom mastectomy button-down tops that had built-in, interior pouches to hold the drains, or (2) a regular button-down shirt with a special belt that held the drains (think fanny pack).

Having the drains removed enabled me to start feeling like myself again, and I became encouraged and positive as Brian and I sat in the waiting room at MSK. Even though I did not know all the nuances regarding my type of cancer, I was hopeful about the potential of not requiring chemotherapy since all the cancer had been removed from my body and had not spread into the lymph nodes.

After two hours of waiting in the lobby, we met with the doctor, and my happiness dissipated as I learned about the recommended next step.

The doctor confirmed that while the cancer had

successfully been removed from my body, chemotherapy would be highly recommended in order to treat any potential existing cancer cells circulating throughout my body.

It was one of my greatest fears, and yet, as much as I hated the idea of chemotherapy, the thought of having lingering cells in my body was a worse thought.

The doctor continued to explain the best two chemo treatments for my situation: (1) CMF (Cyclophosphamide, Methotrexate, and Fluorouracil) infusion which consisted of one treatment every three weeks for a total eight cycles, which would reduce the return rate to approximately 9.9%-10%, or (2) TC (Taxotere and Cyclophosphamide) infusion which consisted of one treatment every three weeks for a total of four cycles, which would reduce the return rate to approximately 9.8%. If I opted out of chemo altogether, the return rate would be approximately 20%.

It was clear that chemo was the next hurdle to cross, but I felt a little unclear on which specific treatment was ideal for me. While the second option seemed like the obvious, best answer, since it was shorter cycles, the downside was that I would most likely lose my hair: a major side effect that I was trying to avoid.

However, my doctor advised TC, the more aggressive treatment, adding that many of her patients had success with the cold capping process which is designed to help prevent hair loss. She allowed me to try on the different sized caps to see if it was something I would like to consider and determine which size would be best for me.

While I tried on the different silicone caps, the doctor further described how this advanced form of technology worked. She showed me the interior lining of the cap, a layer of high grade silicone that contained a gel-type liquid within, and when fitted to one's head and plugged into the proper cooling machine at the treatment center, the gel cools the hair follicles on the scalp, causing them to go into hibernation, and ultimately, stop the chemotherapy from touching the root.[6]

Additionally, she explained that even though it would be rare to lose my hair with the CMF treatment, she had seen patients use the cold cap as a form of extra precaution.

At that point, I was leaning towards the CMF treatment, as it would enable me to keep my hair. The doctor agreed that it would be a good treatment for me, but knowing my appointment with the other oncologist was only a week away, I decided to wait and hear what that doctor would say. However, in the meantime, I decided to make the most of my time at the MSK office and get fitted for a cold cap. Whether it was CMF or TC that was best for me, I was unsure, but I did know that I wanted to put forth every effort of salvaging

---

6. *Penguin Cold Caps*, n.d., https://penguincoldcaps.com/.

my hair throughout this process, so ordering a cold cap was next on my list.

Prior to concluding our meeting with the doctor, she asked if I would be doing treatments at their satellite center in New Jersey, and I responded by informing her that I would most likely continue treatments back in Florida.

Even though both Brian and I prayed that chemo wasn't necessary, we'd decided that if it was required then it would be best to head back to the warm weather and be at our own house for treatments, especially if the treatments were for a long duration of time.

With that decision in place, my doctor gave me the name of a recommended oncologist in the Boca Raton area in Florida and emphasized the importance of starting treatment six to eight weeks post surgery.

That time frame felt very tight and somewhat impossible to achieve considering I would not have clearance to travel until the six-week mark of my surgery. My head started to spin thinking about all the details that needed to perfectly fall into place, but I took a deep breath, reminding myself that God was in control, and focused on the things I could control in that moment. It was well past 5:00pm in New York, so dialing up the oncologist in Florida would have to wait until the following day.

While the overall information I had learned from that

meeting was disappointing, since chemo was something I was really hoping to avoid, the good news was that neither one of the infusions would require a port. They both could be administered using a vein in my arm. I was thrilled to hear that news because I had heard nightmare stories about the port placing process.

As Brian and I retrieved the car from the nearby parking garage and made our way out of the city and back to my parents' house in New Jersey, we called a few close friends and shared the updates with them. I cringed every time we spoke the word chemo, but at the same time, I knew the inevitable treatment was the best course of action for my long-term health.

After the phone calls ended, I found myself silently staring out the car window with the pillow strategically intact between my chest and the seatbelt and worship music from The Message SiriusXM channel playing softly in the background. Brian recognized my quiet demeanor and asked what I was thinking about. I told him I was bummed about the news regarding chemo but was focused on the good news extracted from the meeting: I had an option that would allow me to keep my hair, and I did not need a port.

He agreed that those where positive aspects about my situation and said that it would be good to hear the second doctor's options and suggestions.

The next morning had a little déjà vu feeling as I set my alarm for 9:00am to call another oncologist's office, but this time it was for a doctor in Florida. The secretary was extremely kind and helped me secure an appointment within the next two weeks, which would mark week four post-surgery. Even though I had not yet received travel clearance from my plastic surgeon, I impulsively agreed to the appointment thinking time was of the essence.

I had no idea how I was going to fly to Florida, meet with the oncologist, fly back to New Jersey, pack my bags (without straining, stretching, or lifting anything heavy with my arms), return to Florida, and start my first chemo infusion within the next two weeks, but a piece of me knew that God would help me figure out a way.

# CHAPTER
# SEVEN

Sure enough, God paved the way in helping me heal quickly and tackle another full week of doctor appointments. My weekly visit with the plastic surgeon was productive and efficient, as usual, and with the excellent healing condition of the incision sights, my doctor granted me permission to travel to Florida for two days to meet with the oncologist.

With a little pep in my step, I felt encouraged as Brian and I walked into the meeting with my second oncologist at Cooperman Barnabas Medical Center in New Jersey. I felt equipped with information from my first oncologist visit and assumed this doctor would repeat the same treatment options for my situation.

Wrong assumption. Although this oncologist provided

me with the same two options, the lighter CMF and the more intense TC, she heavily emphasized how she thought the TC treatment would be best for me. She said that if I were her daughter, she would want me to do TC being that triple negative is such an aggressive form of breast cancer.

I appreciated that personal touch of advice, as I felt as though she genuinely cared about my condition. Additionally, I gravitated towards her energetic, sympathetic, witty personality which I later learned was a rarity when dealing with doctors in the cancer line of work.

We thanked the doctor for her time and valuable advice, and let her know that we would be in touch shortly with a decision. She provided us with her contact information and offered to communicate any decisions to my oncologist in Florida. That piece of information was music to my ears and a blessing to be added to my journal, as the doctor phone calls, appointments, and record requests were becoming slightly overwhelming.

The car ride home felt reminiscent to the ride home from MSK, but for the first time, there seemed to be an unspoken clarity between Brian and myself regarding the best treatment protocol for me, and before I could open my mouth, Brian finished my thoughts.

He shared with me why he thought TC would be the

smartest option for me: (1) the treatment was the shortest - four treatments instead of eight, which would last three months as opposed to six, (2) TC would be more aggressive and effective in halting new growth of any potentially existing cancer cells, and (3) if I cold-capped during all my infusions, it was possible I wouldn't lose all of my hair.

I knew Brian's reasoning was right, and by the time we pulled into my parents' driveway, my mind was made up. TC would be my selected treatment.

We recapped the information to my parents, and I grabbed a blanket and curled up in my special, recliner-lift chair, where I played a few mindless games of Words With Friends before going to sleep.

Within a few days, the cold cap arrived on my doorstep. I followed the process of contacting customer service to have my serial number registered then went through the contents of the box. I found a messenger-style carrying case and a blue, gel-like cap (similar to the texture of a warm ice pack) with a chord extending from the end of it. There was also a grey, foam cap, which would be placed over the gel cap, a white towel, shampoo, conditioner, a spray bottle, mirror, and a cotton headband.

I felt relief at seeing these items, and proceeded to call the company to register my serial number. I learned that almost half the patients who go through TC treatment and cold cap, keep approximately 50% of their hair.[7] For patients with thick hair, losing 50% is not as noticeable, and for patients with thinner hair, they recommend wearing hats to help get through the awkward transition period.

Maintaining 50% sounded promising, though it was hard for me to imagine exactly what that meant. Did that mean my hair would thin evenly over my scalp, making it less noticeable, or did it mean random chunks of hair would fall out, making the loss more obvious? I decided to take the optimistic perspective of my hair evenly thinning.

As I placed everything neatly inside the cold cap carrying case, I thought to myself: *I am more concerned on how my body will react to the infusions. If I lose 50% of my hair, I lose my hair.* At the same time, I didn't believe I would lose even that much especially holding onto the words of my doctor that most of her patients have better than expected rates.

With Brian out of town on a business trip, we decided that my mother would accompany me to Florida to meet with the oncologist. Continuing to try for a semblance of normalcy and not wanting to worry about doing my hair with such a tight schedule over the next forty-eight hours, I scheduled my usual blowout.

The next morning, my mother and I headed to Newark Airport, where she dealt with our carry-on luggage, as I

---

7. PAXMAN, "Decision Making Guide," n.d., https://coldcap.com/cold-capping/decision-making-guide/.

couldn't lift anything. The three-hour flight from Newark, New Jersey to Fort Lauderdale, Florida landed just in time for us to grab a bite to eat and arrive, on time, for my oncologist appointment at 3:45pm.

We entered the lobby of the Lynn Cancer Institute in Boca Raton, Florida, where the beautiful building suggested it had been under recent construction, and my mother and I immediately shared our overall positive, first impressions. We passed through the COVID screening check point and made our way upstairs to the hematology oncology department.

A few moments later, we were called into the doctor's office. As we waited for the doctor to arrive, my mother and I discussed questions we had for the doctor, including her recommended date for my first treatment and any additional required protocols before each treatment. Since this was my third oncologist visit, I felt as though I knew all the information surrounding my specific case, aside from confirming dates.

Moments later, however, the doctor arrived, and after introducing herself, she shared her conversation with my oncologist from Cooperman Barnabas Medical Center, and agreeing that TC was the right decision, she began to explain intricate details surrounding my treatments:

1.  I would need to come in for blood work forty-eight hours prior to each infusion.
2.  I would need to take a steroid pill the day before each treatment, as well as, the day after treatment (both morning and night).
3.  I would need to make myself available every three weeks for six hours at a time. This would allow for the administration of my entire "cocktail" of drugs (i.e. Taxotere, Cyclophosphamide, anti-nausea medicine, steroid, and other lovely ingredients I wasn't too keen on knowing).
4.  Cold capping would also require an additional hour prep period before drugs were administered, along with an hour-and-a-half cool down period after infusions were completed.
5.  All drugs would be administered by vein.

Additionally, after each treatment was finished and prior to leaving the infusion department, a nurse would affix a special patch on my arm which was designed to stimulate my white blood cell count. The patch could not get wet, would need to be worn for twenty-four hours, and a steady, red light would indicate when it was safe to remove it. My head was on the brink of explosion trying to feverishly remember all the important details she was spewing. Then, she launched into the laundry list of potential side effects: tiredness, mouth sores, neuropathy in the hands and feet, loss of appetite, constipation, loss of menstrual cycle for up to a year post treatment, potential onset of pre-menopause, loss of hair. The list went on and on.

However, despite the discouraging side effects, I decided that I was not going to waste my energy worrying about which ones I would or would not experience, especially since she made it clear that everyone reacted differently, when finally, she shared some good news:

The oncologist said that since I was young, healthy, and in great shape, she anticipated that I would experience a positive response to the treatments. Hearing that news was promising, however, amongst all the words spoken, I couldn't shake the word neuropathy from my mind. Unsure if it was a nudge from God, I asked the doctor to provide more details on that specific side effect. She responded by explaining that at any point during treatment, I could experience some tingling or numbness in my fingers and toes. The normal nerve sensations would gradually return after completion of the final treatment, and only in very rare instances, did patients experience permanent numbness.

Throughout my previous oncologist visits, this potential side effect had popped-up before, but today, for some reason, it stood out to me, so I continued to inquire. I asked her about the popular patient hack I heard about in order to prevent neuropathy from occurring: placing the hands and feet on ice packs during the time frame when the TC drugs were administered. She said that decision was ultimately up to me, considering there was no hard, scientific evidence backing up that protocol, and she had patients who followed that advice and still experienced neuropathy.

I found myself in a small conundrum, but once again, I decided that I was going to do everything I possibly could to eliminate this side effect from happening to me. This meant putting my hands and feet on ice for the two hours during treatments and leaving the rest in God's hands.

We returned to New Jersey with a plan and a date – October 5, 2021 (six weeks post-surgery). This left me ten days to pack up three months' worth of belongings from my parents' house, fly to our house in Florida, unpack, and prepare for treatment number one.

I made my last pre-treatment appointment with my plastic surgeon, and found myself getting emotional. He and his PA played such an intricate role in my cancer journey: masterfully piecing me back together and following the weekly progress of my healing with professional love and care; something I would never forget.

I shared my concerns regarding chemo, and he assured me that I would do great and that he and his team would be waiting for me, ready to plan my second surgery (exchanging the temporary tissue expanders with permanent implants) whenever I was ready. I was reminded of God placing people in my life before, to say exactly the right words at exactly the right time. Once again, my doctor's supportive words were precisely what I needed to hear.

I was cleared to travel home to Florida, and I left the office feeling good about the positive progress I was making towards closing this chapter in my life.

I was not prepared, however, for the unexpected and abrupt dip of darkness that I would soon fall into.

# CHAPTER
# EIGHT

I returned to my parents' house and immediately set to work packing. Considering the weeks' worth of clothes, shoes, and cosmetics that decorated every surface of the guest room where Brian and I had been staying, I thought it would be best to kick start the dreaded process at once.

I was strategically organizing my shoes along the bottom portion of the suitcase, when it suddenly occurred to me that my chemo treatment was only seven days away. I set down a pair of Golden Goose sneakers and squatted into a sitting position.

Through the window, colorful hues of fall decorated the tree branches that swayed in the wind, and I thought to myself: *I won't be returning here for at least three months...*

*what will happen in the next three months? What if the chemo makes me sick? What if I do experience neuropathy?*

My breaths shortened, and I quickly experienced the same emotions I had in the salon chair. Tears welled and before I knew it, I was uncontrollably sobbing.

With Brian out of town on a business trip and both my parents out of the house, I felt alone with only my anxiety.

"God," I said aloud. "I can't do this on my own. Help me God. Please, help me."

*Call Brian,* my inner voice spoke back to me.

Melting into the floor, I reached for my phone.

"Hi, Hun!" Brian energetically answered, but I was crying so hard, I couldn't respond.

"Carrie? Are you ok…Carrie, listen to me. It's going to be alright." He instructed me to breathe. And finally, after a minute of his coaxing, I was able to catch my breath and form a proper sentence.

"I'm scared. I'm scared for chemo," I said, and with the utterance of the word, chemo, another round of sobs erupted.

Understanding my moment of panic, Brian asked me to respond to a question. A question he always asked me in order to realign my mind whenever feelings of fear or worry creep inside my head: "Who do you always tell me is in control?"

"God," I managed to respond through a series of short,

quick breaths.

Brian continued: "What have you told me He has done for you so far?"

I knew what he wanted me to say – what I knew to be true: that He had opened incredible doors for me, making sure I had seen the best doctors, making sure my body healed perfectly, and making sure I didn't experience any pain.

"I know He has," I mumbled in response, but with a slight increase of calmness and clarity in my tone.

"You have always told me God has a plan for you Carrie," he continued. "His hand is on your life, and He will not stop being with you and guiding you through chemo."

Knowing how God has used a variety of methods of communication to speak to me in the past: Scripture, songs, nature, internal nudges from the Holy Spirit, and people, I felt this to be a moment where God was using Brian as a vessel to speak directly to my heart

As his words continued to calm my beating heart, my tears surfaced again, only this time as I experienced an overwhelming sense of God's love – love I was embarrassed and ashamed to say, in a moment of such low faith, that I didn't deserve.

Brian seemed to sense the shift, and asked what I was thinking about.

I immediately got choked up but managed to sputter

those words I was afraid to say out loud.

"None of us deserve His love," he said. "That's how great God's mercy and love is for us. It is 100% undeserving love."

I dried my tear-stained cheeks, and eventually returned to a regular rhythm of breathing. Everything Brian said was true, and more importantly, they were words I needed to hear. I thanked him for always being the greatest rock in my life and realigning my faith when it was needed most. He reassured me that he would always be there for me, and we exchanged an *I love you* before hanging up the phone.

I sat on the floor a moment longer digesting what just took place. I couldn't help but replay how the simple process of packing a suitcase quickly turned rogue, but more importantly, I couldn't ignore the overwhelming, undeserving, merciful, and gracious love of God that coursed through my heart.

"Thank you," I said to Him. And then, the most interesting feeling happened. Although the past five minutes had been an emotional roller coaster of a ride, I found myself craving to experience it all over again. That split second rush of Christ's love was contagious. A love that is greater than anyone could ever truly know.

Furthermore, God's immediate response to my prayerful cry about feeling incapable of walking this journey alone was something I wasn't prepared for. I never anticipated His powerful presence being perfectly interwoven through a beautiful promise that Brian referenced:

*"I am with you always." – Matthew 28:20*

# CHAPTER
# NINE

Brian and I boarded the plane to Florida. As I quickly shuffled into my row, allowing fellow passengers to pass by, I found myself once again paranoid. Although I was excited to be heading back home, I realized that it was my first time in weeks being in a confined space with a large group of people, and with only three days left before my first chemo treatment, the thought of getting COVID continued to haunt me.

I sluggishly slid down into the seat, wishing I could push a button that would magically transport me home, rather than remain in close proximity to a few hundred strangers.

I reminded myself to relinquish control to God, and proceeded to do the one thing that always manages to relax me when anxious thoughts try to get the best of me: praise. I plugged in my air pods, turned on my worship playlist, and silently sang to myself as we taxied away from the gate.

The flight was just as I liked, uneventful, and we landed safely at Fort Lauderdale Airport. We retrieved our bags, loaded up the car, and continued onward to our house in Boca Raton.

A smile crossed my face upon seeing the perfectly planted palm trees that lined the main entrance of our gated community. I couldn't help but roll down the car window and breathe in the heat, and for a brief moment, my circumstances seemed to evaporate right out the window and into the tropical air. I had been in the state of Florida for less than one hour, yet, I understood how the year-round, summer-like weather of South Florida provided a sense of healing to both the mind and body.

I was so happy that we had decided to do my chemo treatments in Florida. I envisioned how I now would have the ability to step outside into the beautiful, warm weather at any time and go for a walk or spend time with friends around an outdoor dinner table. This would not have been possible during the typical wintery, snowy Jersey months of October, November, and December. These thoughts were healing to my soul, and even though round one of chemo was right around the corner, I felt a boost of confidence well up inside of me and thought to myself: *You can do this!*

The weekend was designated for two specific activities: getting organized at home and spending time with friends – which felt like years since we had last seen each other. It felt like a blessing that Brian and I had moved into a new home, new development, and new state less than one year ago, and in such a short period, developed a great circle of new friends – the type of friends I felt could be lifelong.

For starters, the people we had met, despite only knowing us for approximately six months, had supported me since the start of my diagnosis and continued to cheer me on from the sidelines as I endured my race.

They had sent me cards, flowers, and text messages daily. They had cooked me meals and prayed for me. All of these individual acts of kindness triggered a specific, emotional feeling of love that I hadn't experienced in years.

Unwittingly, these friendships had even begun to fill a deep void that I'd carried inside my heart ever since high school: a void that I had buried and worked hard at ignoring, yet, had been made to address as it periodically surfaced at different points in my life.

Namely, this void was my callused and bruised heart from years of "mean girl" bullying I had endured in high school which had caused me to be suspicious and cautious towards new friendships.

To this day, the vivid memory of my closest friends in high school, one-by-one, taking their lunch trays and moving to a separate table from where I was seated, leaving me to eat by myself, still strikes a chord of sadness in my heart. In the heat of that moment, it hurt to know that none of the girls felt strong enough to defend me, but it was even more hurtful knowing that the ringleader of the group was my best friend at the time.

My twenties hadn't been much different, as I negotiated through catty and manipulative behaviors from other women, the one difference being that I had learned how to properly manage my expectations of different types of friendships.

I had come to understand that there will be friends in life that can't fulfill the loyal, "there for you through thick and thin" friendship simply because they do not know how. It is not part of their DNA. These are the types of friends who may have known how to make me laugh and have a fun time, but when life fell apart and I needed an ear to listen, I could not rely on them. Their response to those types of conversations was often surface deep, casual, and handled in a way that either made light of the issue at hand or redirected the conversation back to themselves.

While I had come to be disappointed by those types of friends, I had also learned to accept these relationships, and these women, for who they were. This did not mean I couldn't continue to be friends with them, it just meant that I had to manage my expectations of the kind of friendship they offered.

As I witnessed the outpouring of love from my new friends in Florida, I felt blessed that I had finally found genuine, caring people. I believed that it was not by chance that God answered this secret desire in my heart by planting me amongst a community of people that He knew I longed for. Additionally, He knew that being in Florida for the next few months of my treatment – surrounded by both the warm weather and love of friends – was exactly where I needed to be.

I spent the weekend leading up to my first treatment relaxing, working out, socializing, and trying not to think about the looming, potential side effects of TC chemotherapy: exhaustion, nausea, mouth sores, constipation, diarrhea, sleep deprivation, loss of appetite; the list seemed endless.

At 8:00am, Brian packed up the car with all my belongings that were sitting by the front door: a small cooler containing the ice packs for my hands and feet, the cold cap gear, and a large tote bag filled with various pillows and blankets that had been gifted to me from friends. Feeling positive and ready to conquer the day ahead, Brian and I got into the car, turned on The Message SiriusXM channel, and punched in the address to the Lynn Cancer Institute.

The first ten minutes of the drive consisted mostly of Brian and I silently listening to the inspirational music emanating through the speakers of the car, when suddenly, a particular song came on and caught my attention. It was a song I had heard many times before, but I truly felt as though God was playing it on purpose for me that morning. It was similar to the feeling I had during the previous week, when I felt God communicating with me through the phone conversation with Brian.

I turned the volume up a notch and intently listened to the lyrics that Hillsong UNITED sang:

*"When the road runs dead*
*You can see a way I don't*
*And it makes no sense*
*But You say that's what faith is for*
*When I see a flood You see a promise*
*When I see a grave You see a door*
*And when I'm at my end*
*You see where the future starts."*

While the above verse perfectly encapsulates the limited, human perspective I was facing in this battle, compared to the Omniscient capability of our God, it was the words in the following chorus that drew me closer:

*"I don't know how You make a way*
*But I know You will*
*I don't know how You make a way*
*But I know You will."*

The repetition of that simple phrase calmed me, as I knew God would make a way; yet, at the same time, I wasn't looking forward to the physical toll I would need to endure over the next few days.

# CHAPTER
# TEN

Twenty minutes later, we pulled into the parking lot of the cancer center, and a strange feeling overcame me, and my inner voice sounded:

*Record this moment.*

Brian reached for the door handle when I grabbed his arm. "Can you film a quick video of me on my phone?" I asked.

"Sure," he said, outstretching his hand.

I handed him my phone when the feeling grew stronger. "If you could stand outside your door and film me in my seat, that would be perfect," I said.

Brian assumed the position as camera man outside the driver's car door, and I turned sideways in my seat to face him, smoothing over my washed and styled hair. I was unsure of the exact words to say, but as I opened my mouth, the voice inside – that of my connection to the Holy Spirit – began to guide me.

*Transparency* was the word that came to me, and I went with it, deciding I was going to be completely frank and open to publicly share my cancer story from that point forward. Recording that video signified my commitment to God to reflect positivity, faith, and glorify Him despite the stormy seas I may be walking through. I was convicted to be light in a dark world. I wanted people to know that regardless of the pain or hardship they may be experiencing, they were not alone.

The video elaborated on how a specific Scripture, 2 Chronicles 7:1-3 – King Solomon's dedication of the temple of the Lord – illuminated the powerful and tangible presence of God in my life and reminded me how I serve a good and faithful God.

2 Chronicles 6:40-7:1 says: "Now, my God, may your eyes be open and your ears attentive to the prayers offered in this place. When Solomon finished praying, fire came down from heaven…and the glory of the Lord filled the temple." The Bible continues to describe how the temple was so dense with God's presence that it was not possible for any outsiders to enter.

Imagining this scene taking place caused me to reflect on the moments during my journey when I could feel God's palpable presence. The more I meditated on this Scripture, the more I couldn't help but feel I might be having a similar reaction to the Israelites who witnessed this miraculous event in chapter 7 verse 3: "they worshipped and gave thanks to the Lord saying, 'He is good; his love endures forever.'" Instead of the Israelites being scared or doubtful of what exactly was taking place, their immediate response was to trust and worship Him. Despite the storms in life, I felt the importance of keeping a perspective of praise towards God, knowing He is a good and relentlessly loving God.

I spoke for five minutes, uninhibited, and when I finished, I posted the video to Facebook and headed into the building. With COVID protocols in full effect at the cancer center, Brian could only stay a few minutes to help get me situated, then he had to leave.

I noticed how he felt bad leaving me alone, but I told him how I felt strong and ready to tackle the day ahead and reassured him that I technically wasn't alone: God would be with me the entire time.

That slice of truth brought a peace to both of our hearts, and after a quick mask-to-mask kiss, Brian left, and I took my position in the chemo chair.

As I sat, with the IV hooked up, the cold cap strapped on

tight, and the ice packs securely wrapped around my hands and feet, I reached for my phone and became completely overwhelmed with emotions as hundreds of "likes," views, and comments started to flood my Facebook post:

*"Precious Carrie. Your words are such an inspiring acknowledgment of God's powerful and enduring presence in our lives. You are certainly in our prayers during this chapter of your healing. We love you!"*

*"Beautiful, well put Carrie! Your faith and peace you are carrying is building others."*

*"Carrie, although we have not yet met in person, I have been following your journey, praying for your recovery, and hung on EVERY word you said in this video (with tears in my eyes). Your strength and faith will carry you through this. You are truly an inspiration."*

Sharing that video on social media incidentally became the very balm I needed for my soul. It was not only comforting to know that hundreds of people were thinking about me, praying for me, and journeying along with me, but inspiring to see that the power of my words connected and engaged with viewers.

My faith level grew and I became ever more motivated to keep my eyes on Jesus and stay committed to the practice of *walking by faith and not by sight*.[8] For the sake of my own wellbeing, and to connect with others, I had the distinct feeling I would be Called again to continue documenting.

Over the next six hours, the tag team of nurses monitored me closely, popping in and out of my room every fifteen minutes. I was grateful the first fifteen minutes had come and gone without much activity, as the nurses advised that if I had an indication of an allergic reaction to the chemo drugs – rash around the IV site or pain in my neck or back – it would happen within those first few minutes.

As I continued to sit in the chair, surveying any signs of abnormalities with my body, I realized the next six hours would not be as comfortable as I imagined. The discomfort was not because of the actual chair itself, as it was a cushiony, La-Z-boy-styled chair adorned with soft, down pillows I'd brought and warm blankets the nurses draped over my legs, nor was it from the thought of injecting "poisonous" chemicals into my body, as I didn't think that way. In fact, as I sat there staring at the IV in my arm, I thanked God for putting me in that chair and successfully bringing me to this moment, as it signified that I was one step closer to being finished.

---

8. 2 Corinthians 5:7. ESV.

The real discomfort came from knowing I had very few options to pass the time. I thought I would be able to use my computer to get work done, but between the nurse's request that my IV arm remain still and the few hours during which my hands had to be placed on ice, I could barely type. I thought I would be able to plug in my air pods and listen to music or make phone calls, but having the cold cap strapped tightly around my head and ears made that impossible. I considered making calls on speaker phone or via FaceTime, but knew this would disturb other patients and enable them to hear my private conversations – not an option.

Reading a book would have been nice, but I had forgotten to pack one. So, with my one free hand, I picked up my phone and continued to find comfort by scrolling through the comments and loving emojis my friends shared on Facebook.

Around 2:00pm, Brian returned to help me pack up all my belongings and bring me home. On our way out, we stopped at the scheduling desk to select the date and time for my next treatment in late October.

I left the building feeling encouraged from the outpouring of support on Facebook and relieved that I had successfully made it through my first treatment with no immediate reactions, thinking, *1 down, 3 more to go!*

Feeling grateful and in a positive state of mind, I began to pray, asking God for my body to continue to respond well to the treatment. I knew that there were so many things that could go wrong post treatments, so I was bracing for the worst-case scenario.

At home, as I unpacked my bags, I replayed the recent instructions from the nurse: drink at least sixty-five ounces of water each day; do not consume any alcohol; do not consume any pomegranate fruit or juice (to avoid a potential interaction with the chemo); do not consume any raw foods (i.e. sushi, egg, meat, etc.); contact the doctor with signs of a fever; expect any changes in hair loss/thinning to be most prevalent days 17-19 post treatment; and, any side effects I experience post treatment one, would be a good indication of the side effects I would experience for the remaining three treatments.

To say that I was hyper monitoring my body over the following few days would be an understatement. Each day, I carefully logged my water intake, sleep time, condition of my appetite, any indication of fever, rashes, or reactive skin, joint pain, and of course, though the vainest of worries, I admittedly continued to care about any thinning of my hair.

I moved through my house over the next three days, stopping at mirrors, relieved each time to see I was doing well. The only real side effect I felt was exhaustion.

"Can I get you anything?" Brian would ask, as I lay on the couch for hours at a time, something I had never done before in the history of our marriage. But sleep was the one thing my body was requiring of me, and I gave in as needed, moving from couch to bed, and back to the couch.

Those first few days I found I was so tired. I didn't have the energy to read my Bible, to stay awake to binge watch a mindless television show, let alone prep a small meal. Brian came to the rescue, cooking delicious, nutrient dense meals, and I found myself literally thanking God for all the small things that seemed to be going right – like that I still had an appetite, and wasn't nauseous or sick. Every time I brushed my teeth, I thanked God that I hadn't developed mouth sores. Every time I passed a mirror, I thanked God for the hair on my head.

Before I knew it, day four had arrived and I felt as though my period of walking on eggshells had passed, and I rose from bed and grabbed my phone. I opened the Notes app, and logged how day four was what Brian coined the "turn the corner day" for me. Feeling energized and determined to do everything possible to remain strong throughout this period, I laced up my sneakers and went for a long walk.

Passing beneath the blue sky and palm trees, I once again thanked God for my health. And for a moment, it felt funny to convey this, as I knew the medical world had classified me as sick and unhealthy having been diagnosed with cancer and currently undergoing chemo treatments. However,

I felt healthy and strong, and I contributed this feeling to the previous years of being diligent about nutrition, diet, and exercise. So, instead of allowing the classifications and opinions of others determine the status of my health, I decided to focus on what I believed to be true.

Back inside, I got ready for the day. I saw small amounts of shedding in my hairbrush, but I felt it was nothing to be alarmed about, as I was convinced that the worst of chemo side effects had clearly passed me by.

Additionally, I was encouraged in thinking that if this was what my general recovery experience would resemble, then overseeing the annual conference my husband and I hosted annually for 300 people in Palm Beach should not be an issue. The conference fell in November, always overlapping with my birthday, and that year, it would end one day before chemo treatment number three.

The timing for me to resume working was perfect, I reasoned, because the medical team had informed me both my energy and body were at its peak in the third week post chemo: my body had sufficient time to recover, rebuild its white blood cell count (the immune systems major form of defense), and prepare itself for the next infusion.

What I did not know was that despite how good I may have physically felt throughout that initial recovery period, my weakest – lowest immune days – were between days seven and ten.

One week after my first treatment, I went for my first round of follow-up blood work. Sitting in the blood drawing chair of the lab at the Lynn Cancer Center with my arm draped over the adjustable arm rest, I chatted with the nurse and when asked, I shared how healthy and strong I had felt over the past few days. She was so happy to hear that news, and after the vials were filled, she escorted me to the doctor's exam room and instructed me to wait there, as the doctor would be in shortly to review my results.

A few moments later, I was greeted by the kind face of my doctor. As she sat down across from me, she asked how I was feeling and wanted an update on any side effects I had been experiencing over the past week. After I shared the good news, she proceeded to pull up my lab results and explained how she would like me to be extra careful over the next two to three days. She requested that I avoid grocery shopping, seeing friends, or any other people outside my immediate family.

Her comment struck me as odd because I felt great. She continued to explain that my neutrophil levels (white blood cell count) were .7 and normal range was between 1.5 and 2.0.

In other words, I essentially had no immune system.

My doctor said this was normal, as the chemo wipes out

neutrophils, and then the body takes a few days to rebuild back to normal levels. She continued to explain the purpose of the patch I wore on my arm for 24 hours post treatment: to stimulate the body to reproduce white blood cells at a more rapid rate. She also emphasized the importance of not eating any raw foods throughout my entire treatment period, but especially over these next few days, as I would have a very high risk of contracting any sort of bacterial infection.

While a part of me was shocked by this information, once again, I thought about how truly grateful I was to have my health.

My doctor said she would like me to come back in another week – two weeks post treatment – for another benchmark of my levels. I scheduled the appointment for October 18, 2021 and returned home to isolate myself for the next forty-eight hours.

Over the next three days of hermitizing, I again knew I wasn't really alone, and decided to take this ideal opportunity to talk to Him, and remembering my pastor's words, asked what He was trying to teach me through this experience.

Once again, that inner voice surfaced, and filled my heart. This time I heard: *Share your story.*

Reflecting on those three words was funny to me because the first book I ever wrote was entitled, *Your Story for His Glory*, which was a compilation of my personal journal entries – sharing my story– in hopes to encourage others to do the same and share their stories. Suddenly, it seemed as though the concept of me *sharing my story* has become a kind of anthem to my life's message, and the more I mediated on this thought, the more I realized that it only seemed right to continue to openly document my journey.

I grabbed my notebook and began writing, and writing. Those three days of being forced to live as an introvert produced a revelation inside of me where I decided to create my second devotional series, in video, for the YouVersion Bible App, in Italian. The series would be called *Trovare Pace nella Tempesta* (Finding Peace in the Storm), and I would share my faith journey during this current storm I was walking through.

Even though I was fully aware of the fact that my audience may not be walking through the exact same storm as me, I believed they could relate to my story in their own, unique way, as everyone has experienced their own seasons of hardship, whether it be a season of addiction, depression, personal insecurity, a relationship crisis, financial crisis, or a career crisis.

To say I was inspired hardly does justice to those few days when the pages of my journal filled with content outlines for videos, and then drafts for individual scripts. The words flowed so fast from my head to my hand, that it was difficult to keep up. I did my best to record all the ideas and story angles that came to mind, and then took a few more days to condense the content into seven, three-to-five-minute video segments.

When I was satisfied with the message and flow of each script, I took a few hours each day to translate them into Italian and then sent them to my friend in Italy for any final edits.

After the final versions were loaded onto my iPad, I designated time into my daily routine to practice my lines. My goal was to record all seven videos within the following three weeks and have everything completed before all our industry friends and family arrived for our big event in Palm Beach. This timeline would allow me to enjoy the event and time with my family without the pressure of having an unfinished project lurking. It also provided enough time for the videos to be properly produced and queued up for a January 2022 launch.

However, all of this assumed that the next chemo treatment would go smoothly, and that my side effects would be minimal, mirroring my first experience. Hopefully, I would not contract any other illness, and everything would fall nicely into place.

Keeping a positive mindset and reminding myself that God was in control, I made my way into my closet to select potential outfits for the video shoot. After grabbing a few possibilities and laying them out on the bed, I stood there laughing at the pieces I had chosen. It was funny, because despite the fact of it being sunny and eighty degrees in Florida, I had pulled a variety of sweaters, long sleeve tops, and pants from the closet. Clearly, my mood for the series was set to reflect a true Fall vibe – my favorite season of the year.

As I gathered the final selections and hung them up in a designated corner of my closet, I turned and caught a glimpse of myself in the full-size mirror leaning against the wall just outside my closet. Seeing my reflection, I stopped, and realized I had to address another key aspect of my wardrobe look: my hair.

Although my hair did not look different to the average person, I knew it was in a fragile state. As I gently ran my fingers through it and tucked it behind my ears, casually posing a few times to see optimal angles for filming, the advice from the Paxman cold cap customer service representative from a few weeks back played in my head: that it was highly recommended that chemo patients eliminate the use of any hair products or hot tools (including a blow dryer), as it would cause excess stress on the scalp and shorten the life span of hair follicles.

I must admit, I understood the concept of eliminating

repetitive, pulling motions from a brush or harsh chemical products, but the thought of not using a hair dryer seemed a little extreme to me. What damage could hot or warm air on a low setting do? The thought of shooting these videos without somehow styling my hair seemed impossible.

But wanting to follow the professional's advice, I decided to grab my wig and see what it would look like on. Although I had purchased it with the thought of "for emergency purposes only," I stood there thinking to myself:

*Maybe I should start wearing it a little bit now and allow people to get used to seeing me in it in case something drastic were to happen?*

As I gently brushed my hair back, secured the wig on top of my head, and tucked away any stray pieces of hair under the fine netting of the wig, I couldn't help but take in the reality of the situation: that for some period of time in the near future, I might become dependent on wearing the wig. The thought was sobering.

I stared a moment longer and reflected how recording my previous video series for the YouVersion Bible App. last year had been so different with my blowout bookings. Now I had a pile of fake hair hanging down on all sides of my head.

I took off the wig, and this time, held my hair back while trying to envision myself without any hair, bald.

The image I saw in my mind produced a lump in my

throat, and I proceeded to face another unpleasant thought: whether I would be pretty *without* hair.

The tears came instantly, as I hurriedly wiped them away, I suddenly felt too embarrassed to look at myself in the mirror.

*But why?* I wondered.

Confidence and security had never previously been an issue for me – at least that's what I believed to be true, so I remained confused with the mixed emotions circulating inside of me.

Then I felt a sudden shock, as if a band-aid had been ripped away from my bare ego, and the truth remained.

I dabbed my eyes to stop the eyeliner and mascara from smudging, realizing how sometimes it isn't until something is taken away that one realizes the hard truth of a situation.

In that moment, I awakened to the fact of how much I depended on my hair as a source of security and beauty, and now, that very thing was slipping through my fingers, quite literally.

Trying to accept this new reality, I put the wig back on my head, forced a smile through my puffy, red eyes, and focused on something positive to help boost my mood.

I spoke the first thought that came to mind:

"Thank you, Jesus. Thank you for helping me select an incredible wig that is almost identical to my original hair color and style."

Lingering on that slice of gratitude within my heart while adjusting the wig, I decided to move forth with wearing it for the video series to guarantee a consistent look – should my hair become even more fragile.

Walking away from the mirror, I headed back into the living room, grabbed my iPad and reviewed the lines for each video.

The first video, "Tieni il conto delle tue benedizioni" (Count Your Blessings), outlined the importance of posturing your perspective each day, and explained how the daily exercise of writing three things one is grateful for, serves as a strong piece of armor when battling against fear and hardship.

"Ricordare le promesse di Dio" (Recall God's Promises), the second video, would highlight how meditating on God's Word and His Promises brings an unsurmountable peace inside one's heart.

The third video, "Messaggiare su WhatsApp con Dio," (Messaging on WhatsApp with God), would explain the power of having an intimate prayer life with God, while video four, "Cerca un consiglio saggio" (Seek Wise Council), would underline the importance of having an established community of like-minded, trust-worthy, faith-based people and how it can strengthen, challenge, and help one walk through hard times.

"Agite" (Take Action), the fifth video, would underscore how faith without action – living out what one believes – is essentially dead faith. Faith is meant to be lived, shared, and witnessed, even when it is uncomfortable.

The sixth, "Cambia la tua prospettiva da 'perchè io?' a 'insegnami!'" (Change Your Prospective from 'Why me?' to 'Teach me!'), would challenge the listener to do exactly what I had been challenging myself to do each day throughout this journey – asking God to teach me, despite whatever negative or difficult circumstances may come my way.

The final video message, "Condividere la tua storia" (Share Your Story), I knew would be my favorite video as it reflected my recently discovered life's motto: the power and impact sharing your story can have on the lives of others.

As I worked, the weeks flew by, and more importantly, the more time I spent on crafting this series, the more I was awakened to the multi-faceted purpose they served. These videos not only served an immediate purpose of keeping me away from large groups – protecting my lack of immune system – and usurping my attention to prevent my mind from worrying about the details of cancer, but it was amazing to see how this series helped contribute to my bigger Calling: my ministry focused on the Italian culture. This video series kept me rooted in my faith and functioned as a tool for me to share my story with others – this project made me feel as though I was fulfilling a specific purpose that God had for me during this season of my life.

I was engrossed with the production of these videos and relished in the feeling of being used by God to share my cancer journey and glorify Him, in this special way. Everything seemed to be on course, until the simplest, habitual gesture would catch me off guard.

# CHAPTER
# ELEVEN

B ack at the Lynn Cancer Institute, I sat in the doctor's office, anxiously awaiting my most recent lab results, when my nurse came bursting through the door with her energetic self.

"Perfect!" she said, smiling wide.

I breathed a sigh of relief at this exact descriptive word my type-A personality needed to hear.

Continuing to talk in her sweet, excited tone, she explained that my neutrophil level "rallied big time," as it was now 9.1, and since everything looked great, I was approved to move forward with my second treatment.

I left her office, feeling as though I had just received "Student of the Month" status. I sent a quick prayer of thanksgiving up to God and headed home to pack and relax before my second treatment the following day.

I showered, organized my things, logged my meals for my nutritionist to review, and felt a sense of calmness regarding my new chemo-prep routine. However, there was a small glitch in the schedule of this second routine: Brian had to travel for an important speaking engagement, which meant that he could pick me up after my treatment finished, but not drive me there. With my doctors' explicit instructions for me not to drive on the day of treatment, I needed a ride.

Thankfully, my sweet neighbor volunteered to take me and agreed to pick me up promptly at 8:15am.

I woke up early, put on comfy sweats, and sat at the kitchen counter, fueling up on my favorite oatmeal recipe: Bob's Rolled Oats mixed with chia seeds, flax, walnuts, sprouted pumpkin seeds, and a drizzle of honey. As I sat there eating, I started to pray and mentally prepare myself for the day ahead, when suddenly, midway through my conversation with God, I felt the urge to record another video for Facebook.

With all the positive feedback received from the first video, I couldn't help but reflect on the beautiful power that social media platforms can provide, reaching an infinite amount of people. A voice inside of me said, *If you can reach just **one** person with your story, and help them grow stronger in their faith, then it would be worth all your efforts and* *vulnerability.*

With fifteen minutes left before my neighbor arrived, I tossed the empty bowl into the sink and went into the other room to grab my iPhone and travel tripod. The collapsible, light weight tripod was ideal for moments such as this, recording by myself, so I unclipped the legs and set it up in the foyer of our house facing the front door.

As I clicked my phone into the holder and right before hitting the record button, I caught my reflection in the foyer mirror, and let out a sigh of frustration upon seeing that my shoulder length hair had become practically see-through with its thin and sad-looking ends. Knowing that any type of hair tie or clip would pull too hard on the hair and irritate my scalp, I ran to my closet to fetch an adjustable baseball cap. I placed it on my head and gently pulled my hair through the hole in the back, followed by another look in the mirror.

It wasn't perfect, but it was much better, so I turned back to recording the video. Though I had no idea of what I was going to say in my video, I hit "record" and knew the Holy Spirit would load my lips with the right words to speak.

Before I knew it, the concept of transparency had reappeared in the forefront of my mind, and I started to share how the past few days had been some of the most difficult and stressful days of my life. I explained how losing my hair and developing two large bald spots in the back of my head was much harder than I ever could have imagined.

I shared the statistic of how "people who cold cap while undergoing TC treatment are 46% likely to retain 50% of their hair," and how I liked to categorize myself within that 46%,[9] but unfortunately, that wasn't the case.

Luke 12:7 popped into my mind, and I concluded the message by describing how this particular passage had brought healing to my soul: *"Indeed, the very hairs of your head are all numbered. Don't be afraid; you are worth more than many sparrows."*

Referencing that Scripture verse caused a revelation of God's powerful presence within me, and I continued to explain what was on my heart: if God knows every hair on my head, then He must also know every hair falling out of my head. This must mean that He is here with me, experiencing this pain and hardship with me, and more importantly, equipping me with the strength I need to get through it.

Similar to how God's presence filled the temple that Solomon built, I could feel His presence fill my heart and practically hear the words of encouragement: "We will get through this together," just as my neighbor rang my doorbell.

I ended the recording, gathered my things, and decided to edit and post once in the chemo chair.

---

9. PAXMAN, "Decision Making Guide," n.d., https://coldcap.com/cold-capping/decision-making-guide/.

I stepped outside and saw that her "chauffeur service" was nothing less than a five-star experience, as she had taken the time to back out of her driveway, directly adjacent to ours, and pull into my driveway in order to get as close as possible to my front door.

Always carrying a bright smile and high dose of contagious, positive energy, she popped out of her car and helped me load the bags. I thanked her again for driving me and smiled thinking how my kind, bubbly friend was the exact person I needed to escort me to treatment that morning.

Arriving on time, I went up to the second floor, the infusion department, and was so happy to see the same nurses from the previous visit were assigned to my room. I asked them if there was any way I could have them for my remaining two treatments as well, as I found comfort in seeing familiar faces. They made a secret pact, agreeing.

Between the fun car ride with my neighbor and the caring commitment from my nurses, gratitude was the only emotion I could express to God.

As my nurse squad started to organize my room, I followed all the required steps for cold capping. I dampened my hair with water, applied a thin layer of special conditioner, allowing the cap to slide on and off easily, and gently secured a cotton head band around the top of my forehead and over my ears, which prevented the gel-like cap from adhering to my skin. I then affixed the gel-like cap on top of my smooth, wet hair, followed by the gray, foam cap, as an extra source of weight; and finally, I firmly secured the strap from the outer cap beneath my chin. It was definitely not my most fashionable look, as I resembled a cross between a rugby football player and horse racing jockey.

Finally, as I settled in the chemo chair, the nurses administered my IV, turned on the cold cap machine, and initiated the first round of infusions.

Utilizing the time as best as possible, I edited and posted my new video to Facebook, answered some work emails, and made a few phone calls, while being sure to keep the speaker volume on the lowest possible setting.

Once again, I was blown away by the response towards my video.

*"This was so touching. We can feel your emotions through this message. We are here for you. Love you!"*

*"You're amazing and I commend you for being so raw and honest..."*

*"So beautiful and honest. There definitely is someone who needs to hear this. You have a pretty face and smile! Prayers for you and Brian."*

*"Hi Carrie, thank you for that wonderful post and testimony. God has taken the time to count each hair on your head, not because He is bored or has nothing else to do, but to simply demonstrate your great worth in His sight. His call to you is not to be afraid. He is in control of all that goes on in your life and since He cares for the sparrows, He will certainly care for you."*

*"You are so beautiful, Carrie...thank you for sharing. That 'somebody needs to hear this today'...was me. In prayer for you today."*

Tears began to well, as I literally felt God using me as a vessel to minister to others on His behalf – the moments which I live for. I also couldn't believe how much all the Facebook "likes" and comments ministered to my own heart. It was healing to hear encouraging words from friends, family, and especially people I had not spoken to in years.

Consumed with scrolling, reading and responding to all the posts, the hours seemed to fly by, and before I knew it, Brian was on his way to pick me up.

I left the cancer center feeling good, but also wary of experiencing the side effects, however mild they might be. And they were somewhat mild, as once again, the nurses had been right; the first three days after this second treatment were almost identical to the side effects of my first. I lazily rotated between the couch, bed, and kitchen counter, wanting to do nothing more than sleep and eat. From time to time, I considered returning to the studio to record, anxious to move forward with my new project, though knew it was important to rest and allow myself to fully recover. Plus, I had buffered my recording schedule to include these recovery days, so everything felt on track.

Day four, my "turn the corner day," I found myself once again sitting in the leather chair of our family room, sipping a cup of hot water with lemon, and browsing the internet on my laptop. Those first few days of chemo recovery somehow felt like a year, and I was eager to get back in touch with society, so I caught up with a few friends and updated them on my status, then switched gears and began practicing my scripts.

As I worked, I casually ran my hand through my hair, and as I laid my hand back down on the computer keyboard, I saw an abnormal amount of hair resting in the palm of my hand – the amount one might remove from a brush after a few days use.

"Brian?" I called.

Hearing the state of panic in my voice, he came rushing into the room. I showed him the clump of hair, just as I noticed more hair resting on the sleeve of my sweatshirt. My eyes trailed over my sweatshirt, where dozens of lose strands covered the surface of my hoodie. Beside me, more strands covered the top of the leather seat cushion. Worse, my scalp seemed to be shedding more hair with the smallest movement of my head.

"How can I help?" Brian asked, likely experiencing his own panic.

"I don't know," I said. "I don't know what to do…I was planning on washing my hair today…but now…" The thought of what would happen with hard water pressure coming down from the shower and hitting my scalp scared me. But even more unnerving was the thoughts of using and form of scrubbing motions to wash my hair.

Our eyes locked, and I think we were both thinking there was only one solution to the problem: shaving my head – which I wasn't ready for.

"Hopefully this is just the worst of it," I said. Knowing I had another six weeks of treatment in front of me, however, worried me, even as I tried to convince myself there might be a select group of days following treatments when I would shed the most, like I was experiencing now.

Brian was fully supportive of my decision, but before he could say another word, I asked him for a favor.

"Given the fragility of my hair…can you help me wash it?"

"Of course."

I decided then that I would open the shower door and

lie down on the bathroom floor with my head draped over the edge of the shower step, so he could use the handheld shower head, which had less water pressure, to gently wet and shampoo my hair. I explained my plan, emphasizing the word "gently."

He followed me to the bathroom where I placed a towel down on the cold, tile floor and I laid down, draping my hair over the shower step. Brian positioned the hand-held shower head over my hair to let the water slowly dampen it, and I tensely laid there while repetitively telling him to be careful.

After a few stressful minutes, he managed to successfully wash my hair, and handed me a fresh towel to dab my hair dry.

I sat up; feeling a little relieved to have put this event behind me but was not prepared for what I was about to see. I turned around and practically choked seeing the shower drain completely covered by hair.

Over the next two days, the hair shedding would continue to stress me out – perhaps even more than the bilateral mastectomy and more than my first two chemo treatments had. I began feeling ultra-self-conscious with every slight move I made. I began, too, to avoid all potential run-ins with the mirror. I even began to resent wearing the wig, as it produced undesirable heat on top of my scalp. I stayed home, feeling anything but pretty and having no real desire to get dressed up and socialize, but I pushed myself to go out a few times each week. It was important to me that Brian and I felt a type of "normalcy" within our lives.

With Brian flying out of town the next day for a business trip, I thought how it was perfect timing for me to take a deep breath, relax, busy myself with practicing my scripts, and remain optimistic that this was a temporary period that would soon pass.

# CHAPTER
# TWELVE

My morning routine of recording three things I was grateful for felt more imperative than ever, as my faith challenged me to seek the blessings in the most stressful days I had ever experienced, through this simple practice.

Pen in hand and journal on my lap, I wrote down my three blessings for the day: Yes, my hair was shedding like a dog, but I was grateful that I still had hair on top of my head. Yes, I had the potential of losing my eyebrows and eye lashes, but mine were still intact. Yes, I was feeling emotionally stressed, but I felt physically healthy otherwise.

Properly aligning my heart and mind was critical for me, as it kept me from getting caught in the slipstream of *why me* thoughts and hypothetical *what if* situations. More importantly, it reinforced God's presence through this very unpredictable storm and reassured me that He would continue to carry me through everything.

I was successfully able to wait two days without washing my hair, but I as the third day approached with Brian still out of town, I realized that I couldn't wait any longer. Plus, I decided it was unhealthy to allow my circumstances to control me in this way and prevent me from taking normal showers.

Feeling confident and emboldened by my faith, I made my way into the bathroom, turned the shower on, and waited for the water to warm up. As I stepped out of my robe, a slight twinge of panic welled up inside, and so I reached for my phone and dialed Brian.

He quickly answered: "Hi Honey, I am just about to board the plane. I can't wait to see you tonight!"

"Hi. Me too," I responded in a less than enthusiastic voice. "I just wanted to let you know that I am about to get in the shower."

He knew what that meant, and without hesitation, asked: "Are you nervous about washing your hair?"

"Yes."

"I am really sorry this is happening. I hate seeing you so distressed, in fact, I think this is the most stressed I have ever seen you. I don't know what else to say except I am sorry that I can't be there to help you. Will you call me when you're finished?"

"OK." I hung up the phone, took a deep breath, and slowly approached the fogged, shower door. I stepped inside, gently closed the door behind me, and stood under the running water with the front of my body facing the shower head. I remained there for a few minutes, breathing in the steamy air, until eventually, I decided it was time to stop procrastinating and turn around to allow the water to dampen my hair.

I slowly eased my way backwards until I felt the water falling on the top of my shoulders, petrified that the heavy water pressure was going to be too harsh on my hair, I cautiously inched my way backwards until the water reached the top of my head.

Happy I had made it that far, but still unsure of how I was going to shampoo my hair considering the slightest touch was enough to remove a chunk of hair, I reminded myself to take things nice and slow, one step at a time.

Just as I leaned forward to grab the shampoo bottle, what felt like a long, slippery, garden snake, slithered down the length of my back and all the way to the bottom of my foot. I screamed at the top of my lungs. The sensation I had just experienced was disgusting, nasty, and traumatizing.

I quickly turned around to see what it was, and saw the shower drain completely covered in my hair. With such a large amount of hair falling out within seconds of the water hitting my head, I knew washing it was not possible.

I burst into tears and screamed at the top of my lungs a mixed prayer of desperation and love:

"God, please help me…I love you, God…I love you so much…please help me. I need you…I don't know what to do."

Sobbing, I covered my face with my hands and felt my body begin to uncontrollably shake, but amidst the distress, I somehow realized that it would probably be best for me to get out of the shower – eliminating a potentially dangerous accident from happening.

I reached to turn the shower knob to the off position, which took all the energy inside of me. I managed to push the glass door open, but didn't make it far, as I fell directly onto my knees on top of the dry bathmat.

On the bathroom floor, naked, curled over in a child's position, I knew I had reached my absolute rock bottom. Drowning in my brokenness, I hurled out to God one desperate cry for help after another. The words pouring from my mouth were saturated with grieving moans and short, choking breaths so that my words barely articulated. However, all that mattered, is that He could hear as I begged and pleaded with Him to show me His presence.

After what seemed like an hour of silence, I slowly raised my upper body and crawled a few feet until I was able to touch the hem of a towel hanging over a towel bar. With one light tug, it unraveled from the bar, and once in my hands, I slowly wrapped it around my body, feeling as though I were moving in slow motion.

I remained seated on the floor a while longer, as though it had become a safe zone, for I not only was unsure if I had the strength to stand, I knew doing so would require me to face myself in the mirror. However, after a few moments longer, I realized that I had to confront the inevitable.

I let the towel fall away as I maneuvered myself to a seated position on the ledge of the bathtub. I inhaled a deep breath and opened my eyes to see my reflection.

Before I could even fully process who the person was staring back at me, a tsunami of tears erupted down my cheeks. Through the waves of cries and gasping breaths, I found myself thinking: *how is this possible...there is no way that is me...there is just no way...what is going on?*

Large bald spots expanded over the surface of my scalp, like Gollum's from Lord of the Rings. I saw fake, breast tissue expanders that rested beneath the skin of my chest, and the scar on the side of my abdomen from a recent skin procedure. I looked patched up, almost inhuman. I felt ugly and broken.

A cry escaped my lips: loud, desperate, and stemming from a place deep within my soul; a place I never knew existed. A place that could have probably only been revealed in this very moment.

"Please meet me here. I need you," I pleaded to God, trying to calm myself, trying to even out my choking breaths trying not to send myself into a mode of full hyperventilation. But every time I looked at my reflection, it seemed more stunning, horrifying – and embarrassing – to see this most raw, exposed, and vulnerable version of myself that I had ever seen.

I gripped the cold porcelain, feeling completely out of control – a feeling that would take me back to my childhood.

# CHAPTER
# THIRTEEN

Having been diagnosed with epilepsy at the age of two, I spent a good portion of my childhood driving with my mother to different parts of New York City and New Jersey, where we met with a variety of pediatric neurological specialists.

My case was a bit of a mystery, and the doctors worked to solve it, conducting different neurological tests, such as MRIs, sleep deprivation tests, and strobe light tests in order to help determine the underlying cause of my seizures. They also administered varying medication and dosages to control my specific seizure disorder.

My parents tell me how, in the early days, I had a seizure about once a month from the age of two until the age of three. Then, as a result of great medical care and better medicines, the seizures became slightly more controlled. But it wasn't until I was six years old that my seizures became fully controlled.

Those four years were very hard and trying times for my parents, as it was a lot of "trial and error" testing, but more importantly, it tore them apart to witness their daughter suffer in such a way.

As I grew older, the conversation surrounding my childhood epilepsy would arise from time to time, whether a doctor would inquire about the specifics, or a friend might ask about it. I would always have to defer to my parents for information, because I had difficulty remembering details having been so young at the time.

However, I remembered clearly one seizure – occurring when I was five years old – when during a little league soccer game, I ran towards the soccer ball and everything around me went suddenly silent and all I could see was black.

I had no idea how long I had been lying on the ground or what had just happened to me. I remembered trying to open my eyes, but the intense sensation of having five-pound weights attached to my eyelids created a struggle.

The more I forced myself to open my eyes and blink, the more I caught a glimpse of the colors and images surrounding me; but still, I had no idea of my exact location. What was even more baffling is that I couldn't hear anything except for total silence. As I focused hard on my surroundings, I caught a glimpse of people's mouths moving, but could not hear what they were saying. I started to panic and feverishly tried to remember what exactly had happened.

A few seconds later, the silence started to dissipate, and what sounded like a distant legion of voices started to gradually echo around me:

"Carrie, are you alright?"

I thought to myself: *Yes, I am fine!* But as my brain instructed my body to get up off the hot grass of the soccer field, my arms and legs seemed heavy and delayed.

The voices of the people huddled around me became clearer and louder, and I opened my mouth to call out for my mom, yearning for her to come sweep me up off the ground, into her loving arms, and tell me everything was going to be alright, but no words escaped. I tried to yell out her name again but still had difficulty forming words.

Scared, I started to cry, and wondered *How long had I been down?* My last memory was running towards the soccer ball, and somehow, I was now lying on the ground.

I lay helpless and embarrassed on the ground as all my friends stood at a distance and stared at me. The next thing I knew, my mom was kneeling beside me, cradling my head in her arms, and whispering:

"Everything is going to be alright."

Between her calming words and the stares from my friends, I knew exactly what had happened: I had just experienced my first public seizure.

I never understood until now why that particular seizure not only remained one of my earliest childhood memories, but also left a significant mark on my heart, but it makes perfect sense: it was the seizure that marked me as being *different* from all the other kids.

Having never wanting to experience those stares from the soccer field ever again, I innately became determined that I would not be categorized as *different* from the other girls in school. So, for the next fifteen plus years, my behavioral character worked hard at doing just the opposite, fitting in.

Growing up in Rumson, New Jersey was a beautiful and charming experience, but it was the experience of being in a very small town – any sort of drama or fight at school could become the topic of community conversation within hours, and as a result, tarnish one's local reputation.

Over time, this type of societal culture can create a type of pressure where an individual finds the need to gain approval and acceptance from others – and I, for one, was very susceptible, as I spent years spinning my wheels trying to make everyone else happy.

When I think back to my high school years, I think of

how exhausting it was trying to impress the popular circle of girls I hung out with. I think of how I willingly hosted many high-school parties and shuttled people around town, not only because I was one of the first to get my license, but because I wanted to feel important.

I remember begging my mom to buy me the things "every girl in school had." Some of my personal favorites from the list of products included a plaid skirt and knee-high stockings, paired with black, patent leather Mary Jane heels, in order to achieve the coolest *Clueless* look possible; the bright, cheery, 90's swimwear pieces ordered from the coveted J.Crew catalogue of the time; the most comfortable Steve Madden shoe ever designed – the slinky flatform sandal – and of course, whatever the latest trending handbag accessory was at the time: either the Coach duffle bucket bag or the infamous Kate Spade, nylon tote (a.k.a. the diaper bag).

Obviously, my hair style was the final touch to my "look" each day at school, so signing up for a monthly subscription to *Lucky* and *Seventeen Magazine* for hair style inspiration was a no-brainer.

I noted what the top celebrity styles were and experimented with bangs, different color-treated hair, and ultimately, ended up sticking with one of the most iconic haircuts of my generation, until my recent beach wave phase: the Jennifer Aniston, face-framed, layered cut she debuted on the classic television series, F-R-I-E-N-D-S. I enlisted my mother's help in the early mornings to blow-dry my hair in my bathroom to recreate that smooth, professional blowout look that I never could have achieved by myself.

Staying current with fashion, made me feel put together on the outside, enabled me to wear perfectly coordinated outfits when going to school each day, and helped alleviate any possibility of me feeling left out.

However, regardless of which phase of life I was walking through, time and time again, I found that despite my giving two hundred percent of myself, girls inevitably would talk behind my back, ignore me, or worse, purposely sabotage a romantic relationship of mine.

I routinely and subconsciously forgave these girls. I allowed them back into my heart as friends, because those moments of being left by myself at the high school lunch table or the only one not invited to parties, triggered that same feeling from the soccer field: different, and left out, which was not an option for me.

Years went by, and I ended up learning the hard way that the desire to be accepted and liked by others, while emulating a kind, generous heart, is a long and exhausting road; one that invariably leads to a dead end.

While I had experienced my unfulfilled, "dead end" moment well over twenty years earlier, I had decided I would stop living for the approval of others, and instead, focus on living for the approval of my truest friend, God.

But had I achieved this?

As I sat on the edge of the bathroom tub, staring at my broken reflection in the mirror, I realized that a tiny piece of my past was still hanging onto my present self – the piece of me that wanted to impress others, that wanted to present myself a certain way, so that I could fit in.

So that I could be loved.

# CHAPTER
# FOURTEEN

Staring into the mirror, feeling as though I was spinning out of control, I did the only thing I could think of to connect to God: praise.

I reached for my phone, opened my Apple Music App, and pressed the "shuffle" button to my "Worship" playlist.

As the piano keys sounded, I knew it was not by chance that one of my favorite songs had started to play. I immediately felt God's presence densely occupy the space as the overwhelming stillness surrounding me produced an unmistakable, divine, and peaceful silence. Suddenly, what felt like a refreshing cool breeze on a hot summer day swept over my body causing a quick sensation of goose bumps to form on top of the surface of my skin. My mind flashed back to the Scripture I had read about the Israelites in the temple scene of 2 Chronicles, and I stopped crying, stared at my reflection, and listened as God spoke to me through the captivating lyrics of the song *Jireh* by Elevation Worship and Maverick City Music:

*"I'll never be more loved than I am right now*
*Wasn't holding You up*
*So there's nothing I can do to let You down*
*It doesn't take a trophy to make You proud*
*I'll never be more loved than I am right now*

*Going through a storm but I won't go down*
*I hear Your voice*
*Carried in the rhythm of the wind to call me out*
*You would cross and ocean so I wouldn't drown*
*You've never been closer than You are right now*

*You are Jireh*
*You are enough*
*Jireh, You are enough…*

The song continued to play, and I intently listened as the words ministered directly to my soul:

*I'm already loved*
*I'm already chosen*
*I know who I am*
*I know, I know what You've spoken*
*I'm already loved*
*More than I could even fathom*
*And that is enough*
*Yes it is, it's enough, it's enough"*

It was clear: God had heard my pleas of desperation, and was not only meeting me, but comforting me with the exact words of affirmation that I needed to hear:

He loved me.

And His love was enough.

A sense of peace came over me. At the same time, my heartbeat quickened not wanting this serene feeling to end. I told myself to *be still* and relish in His loving presence, and soon, what felt like a warm embrace wrapped around my entire body, and the realizations overcame me:

God's love is not based on the 'perfect beach-wave blowout' I obsess in portraying, nor is it based on the amount of money in my bank account, the number of handbags in my closet, or any other earthly "trophy" for that matter. In fact, there is nothing I could do to make Him love me more than He does right now. His love is an unconditional, unchanging, and relentless love; a love that crossed the ocean of tears and stilled the anxious, drowning waves surrounding me; a love that provided a place of refuge for my weary soul.

As the song continued, my body sat rooted to the cool tile while my mind awakened to the truth that His love had always triumphed over the approval, acceptance, and love of anyone else. It had just taken me thirty-eight years to see it. And now that I did – in this broken, patched up, and raw state – I knew beyond a doubt that He had always seen me as beautiful, for He saw my heart and soul. I also knew that His love was not only enough, but it was also all I needed in life.

I remained still, observing the gentle movement of my chest as I calmly inhaled and exhaled, and listened to one of my favorite verses:

*"If He dresses the lilies*
*With beauty and splendor*
*How much more will He clothe you*
*How much more will He clothe you*
*If He watches over every sparrow*
*How much more does He love you*
*How much more does He love you…"*

The verse from Luke 12:7 immediately surfaced in my mind: *"Indeed, the very hairs of your head are all numbered. Don't be afraid; you are worth more than many sparrows,"* and I felt God reminding me not to forget my worth and value in His eyes.

I sat up a little straighter than before and began to visually scan the upper portion of my broken body; however, this time, I noticed that as my gaze locked with my reflection, something was different. For the first time, I was observing myself with a new confidence; a confidence of self-love that was rooted in truth:

I was a perfectly broken, *loved, and chosen* child of God.

I listened to the beautiful song in its entirety and witnessed my soul experience a sense of rebirth, nourishment, and value that cancelled any previous negative feelings of self-worth. Moreover, I reflected on the powerful, underlying theme of the song – Jahovah Jireh; the Lord will provide – and understood how His love *provides* unshakable peace in the middle of any storm.

As the song ended, I understood the purpose behind the pain of this moment: God was reaffirming that no person, situation, or circumstance can ever take away one's personal relationship with Him.

I stood up, wrapped the towel around my body, and directly confronted my circumstance in the mirror:

"You may have thought you could crush my faith and create distance between me and my God, but you only brought me closer. So, thank you…thank you, cancer."

# CHAPTER
# FIFTEEN

B rian arrived home late that Friday night and I shared the details of the "bathroom scene" – one that will remain one of the most painful yet, beautiful and unforgettable moments of my life – while we decompressed on the couch after a long day of emotional stresses and travel.

While enjoying a glass of Casanova di Neri Brunello di Montalcino wine, from one of our favorite vineyards in Montalcino, Italy, he listened to my reflections about my experience and remarked how he saw a notable shift in my spiritual and personal healing.

He also shared how he believed it was not a coincidence that some of the hardest moments of my cancer journey I had experienced alone, such as walking into the surgery center, receiving chemo treatments, and then having this breakdown moment. Hearing him remind me of this, I remembered the word *teachable* and realized these difficult moments were moments where I had grown the most in my faith.

As our conversation ended, Brian turned to me squarely. "So…does this mean you are ready?"

I knew he had been patiently waiting for me to reach this conclusion on my own, and this time, without hesitation, I responded:

"Yes. I am ready."

We didn't need to say anything more, as we both knew that allowing my hair loss to continue any longer would simply be a form of self-torture. The time had come.

Rising early the next morning, I went through my morning routine, sent the completed video files from my Italian devotional series to my producer, located the business card I needed, and waited patiently until 9:00am − a safe time to text local business owners.

The card was for a local beautician and had been given to me by one of my chemo nurses who, as a cancer survivor, had partnered with the hospital to provide wigs and hair services to cancer patients.

Not knowing the exact logistics of how her services worked, I took a shot in the dark and texted:

*"Hey! It's Carrie Pasch! I wanted to see if you could come do*

*my hair later today? Let me know what works for you* ☺ "

I noticed a lump in my throat had formed while typing the above message, as I couldn't quite bring myself to type the words "shave my head." Without letting myself back out, however, I hit send.

Within seconds, she responded:

*"Good morning. I am at the salon and have a 12:15pm available today if you want to come."*

*"Perfect,"* I wrote. *"I'll see you at 12:15. Thank you so much!"* I hit send, feeling as though a timer had been set.

Over the next two hours, I tried to distract myself with reviewing the final edits of my video project and checking off pending tasks from my "to do" list for our upcoming business event, but as I saw the clock turn 11:00am, I found myself itching to leave the house and get everything over with as soon as possible.

Sensing my urgency, Brian finished up a call and grabbed the car keys.

As we drove to the salon, I tried to relax and mentally prepare for what was about to happen, yet, I couldn't shake my nerves as I tried to anticipate the visual outcome of my head being bald and the emotional impact the entire experience would have on me, so I told myself: "Keep moving forward. God's got you."

After arriving a solid thirty minutes early, we parked the

car, and I grabbed the cashmere, purple and pink, wool blend Gucci beanie hat that was sitting on my lap – a gift Brian had surprised me with from a recent business trip – and walked into the salon.

I checked in at the front desk and within a few minutes my stylist said she was ready to see me. I approached her chair, sat down, and faced the mirror, while Brian sat down in the empty salon chair right beside me. My stylist flung the cape around my body and fastened the clip behind my neck, while beginning to comb through my hair.

An expert stylist and cancer survivor herself, she paid little attention to the clumps of hair quickly clogging the teeth of the comb – something I was highly self-conscious about – and then she asked:

"So, how short would you like to go?"

I looked at my reflection, then made eye contact with her through the mirror, and said:

"Could you do a close cut first, so I can see what I look like before a clean shave?"

"Of course. I will start with a number four," she replied.

I had no clue what that meant, but before I could think anymore about it, she had a pair of scissors in hand and began cutting down the length of my hair – making it easier to shave.

Watching my hair get shorter by the second, my eyes

glassed up, and I tried with all my strength not to blink, which I knew would release the floodgates. So, instead, I stared up at the ceiling, trying to breathe and resist, but the more my hair style transformed into that of a young child's, I couldn't help but release control and allow the tears to freely flow. Not wanting anyone to see, I quickly pulled my arm out from under the cape and wiped my eyes.

When Brian caught sight of my face, he immediately told me how much he loved me and how nothing, including my shaved head, could change his love for me.

Upon hearing his loving and supportive words, my stylist stopped cutting. Then, unexpectedly, she bent down, aligned her head with the height of my shoulders, and while making intentional eye contact with me in the mirror, she whispered:

"This is the hardest step of the entire process, but I promise, you will feel so much better after this is over. You will feel so much lighter."

I was so grateful for her encouraging words in that moment, as I knew they came from a genuine, sharing place, and I thanked Jesus for delivering me into the perfect stylist's hands.

When my beautician was finished with the number four razor, which left about two inches of hair on my head, the three of us took a minute to see what we thought.

After a moment, we all agreed that keeping a little length

actually emphasized the thinness and fragility of my hair and that it would be best to do a close shave.

My beautician switched blades from a number four to a number one and started to run the buzzer from the front of my head to the back. I knew the cut would be over fast, and impulsively told Brian to get out his phone and record this moment.

I figured that since I had been transparent about my entire journey thus far, it would only be right to share the lowest and hardest time too.

As Brian started to film, I tried my best to smile and remain strong for the camera, but with each pass of the razor, my thoughts careened from *You got this and you will feel so much better!* to: *What if you are the part of the rare percentage that experiences permanent hair loss?*

It was as if the devil was working on overdrive to weaken my mental state and throw every punch possible to ruin my faith. There was no doubt in my mind that he knew this was a weak moment for me, possibly the weakest of my entire life, and he was there, in the arena of my mind, trying everything possible to win.

And still, with every negative thought that Satan punched – trying to disorient my thoughts, beliefs, emotions, and steal my joy, hope, and faith – I could feel my faith level rising. With every fearful jab he made, I retaliated with an undercut by professing a blessing that God had made in my life.

Feeling strong and victorious, I sat up a little taller in the salon chair and took in the different angles of my new military-styled buzz cut.

Without hesitation, I ran my hand over the top of my head and observed the new texture: a cross between a smooth crushed velvet and textured, rough sandpaper. Now I understood the meaning behind a number one blade.

My beautician placed a handheld mirror in my hand and spun the chair around so I could view the back of my head. As I looked in the double mirrors, she explained that the "number one" blade is one step above a completely shaved head, and that is why I could still see some bald patches throughout my scalp, however, we all agreed that they were much less obvious with my hair being so short.

She continued to explain that I could eliminate the bald spots by going entirely bald, but I decided that this was enough change for the day.

I thanked her from the bottom of my heart for all her time, kindness, and encouragement, slipped my beanie over my head, and headed outside with Brian.

Once in the sunshine, we turned towards one another, and I smiled as tears of happiness ran down my face.

Brian kissed my forehead. "I am so proud of you," he said. "How are you feeling?"

"Oddly, I feel better," I said. "I no longer have to worry about how my hair looks. She was right…I feel lighter."

We walked to the café next door and sat outside, where I decided to FaceTime my parents.

I knew the sight of their daughter being bald would be difficult, so I braced myself. My father picked up first, and while he was unsuccessful in holding back tears, he managed to mutter a brief yet, loving phrase:

"Oh, honey…I love you so much."

"I love you too Dad," I responded.

We chatted for a few minutes longer and then I hung up to call my mother again. She cried as well, admitting she had always secretly hoped that her experience with cancer was a form of maternal protection – guaranteeing that her daughter would not have to experience the same thing.

I knew this was hard for her to watch, but I promised her that even though this was one of the hardest parts of the journey, I was already feeling better. She said she was happy to hear the genuine tone of happiness in my voice and told me that she would always be there for me.

After we hung up the phone, I felt completely at peace, and I knew I had done the right thing.

I smiled at Brian, and we simultaneously got up from our chairs and headed back to the car.

An hour or so later, Brian and I pulled into our driveway,

and as I stepped out of the car, my phone rang. Thinking my mom had forgotten to tell me something, I quickly swiped to answer the call, and just as I did, I saw that it was one of my neighbors calling. I knew he had been in touch with Brian surrounding the latest series of events happening in my life, so I thought he was calling to check in.

I was right. In his cheerful yet sympathetic tone, he asked how I was doing, but he also wanted to know if Brian and I would be home the following day. Apparently, he and his two sons – and "some other friends" – wanted to stop by.

While the offer seemed vague in my mind, I assumed our friends were looking to cheer me up after the challenging day I had just experienced. So, of course, I told him that I would love for them to come over.

We agreed that 12:00pm would be a convenient time, and I hung up the phone smiling and feeling grateful for the incredible community God had surrounded me with.

However, little did I know the extent of what "a few friends stopping by" meant, and that my friend was planning a special surprise for me – an event unlike anything else I had ever experienced.

# CHAPTER
# SIXTEEN

Sunday morning arrived, and after monitoring my stats post treatment and eating a protein and "healthy fat" enriched breakfast of scrambled eggs and sliced avocado, I felt good, and therefore, decided to go to church.

While I was still trying not to compromise my immune system, a piece of me craved fellowship with others – particularly the fellowship of our church, as I have found nothing comparable to worshipping with a group of fellow believers in front of a live band. Letting the spiritual music flow through my body as I listen to the voices of the congregation rise together, as one body at the altar of Christ, remains one of my favorite activities. For in these moments, the atmosphere shifts, and one can feel the presence of God moving throughout the space. The experience is overpowering and becomes a true testament to God's Word written in Matthew 18:20: *"where two or three gather in my name, there am I among them."*

As Brian and I walked through the doors of the building and took our usual seats, the members of the band assumed their on-stage positions and the instruments began to sound.

As we rose to stand, we both recognized the first few keys of the song and shared a glance. It was my song. The song from my moment with God in the bathroom, and we knew that it was not by mistake that it was playing.

In her beautiful voice, the lead singer took the microphone and started to sing the words from "Jireh" by Elevation Worship and Maverick City Music.

To say I was emotional would be an understatement. I could not stop the tears of joy from running down my face as the Holy Spirit burned inside of me, sending goose bumps throughout my body and reminding me of God's love, provisions, and promises. I smiled and thanked Him for encouraging me to listen to my instinct that morning and come to church.

After the service ended, we headed back home to prepare for our friends.

As Brian and I were setting out some food and beverages, I looked out our back window and saw that a few of the men, their sons, and wives had already arrived. I walked over to the sliding glass door, unlocked it, and went outside to greet everyone. They were already making their way around back, however, as they were trying to respect their distance. I thought that was incredibly thoughtful and told them they could absolutely come inside.

As I was catching up with a few of the ladies, the organizer of the party – the neighbor who had called me the day before – asked if I had a trash bag, bar stool (or one similar), and an extension cord. I didn't think twice about the trash bag, but the request for the bar height chair and extension cord struck me as odd, especially since we already had outdoor furniture.

Regardless, I went inside and fetched the three items. As I returned to the back porch, I saw that a few more people – mostly men – had arrived, capping the group off to about twenty people.

I wanted to ask what this was all about, but by then I was too busy delivering the requested items. I asked my friend where he wanted the chair and he said that in the middle of the grass would be best. Then, as I passed him the bag and extension cord, I immediately noticed an electric razor in his hand. Finally, I asked him what was going on.

Without hesitating, he raised his voice and asked for everyone's attention:

"I think we can all agree that cancer sucks. Today, we are

here to support Carrie and show our love for someone that shouldn't be going through this…we will be with her every step of the way."

I smiled, thanking him for his heartfelt words, and before I had time to think, he spotted Brian in the crowd and yelled:

"Let's go Brian! You are first!"

Brian excitedly walked over and sat in the chair, and I couldn't believe what was about to happen. I ran over to tell him he did not have to do this. I told him that he had such a great head of hair and that he did not have to shave his head for me.

He immediately responded:

"We do everything together! I love you!"

After a quick kiss, our friend switched the head of the razor blade to a number one, matching my cut, and proceeded to shave Brian's head.

I will forever remember the childlike joy and excitement that illuminated my husband's face as he sat in that chair, smiling, clapping his hands, and chanting: "C'mon! Let's go!" while having his head shaved.

A few moments later, his haircut was finished, and he said he felt the excitement and adrenaline run through his body as it was something he had never done before. He rose from the chair, gave me a kiss on my bald head and with a big smile said:

"Now we are twins!"

I hugged him, then heard my friend yelling to the crowd: "Who is next?"

I could not believe my eyes, but over the next hour, every single guy – ranging in ages from thirteen to sixty – sat in that chair and had their heads shaved, for me.

I was in a state of shock and was completely overwhelmed. Some of my neighbors I knew, but only for six months. One couple that attended I had never laid eyes on, let alone had a conversation with, and yet, here they were, the husband sitting in the chair, shaving his head for his future neighbor.

For me, that incredible act of kindness by my friends was the perfect demonstration of the power that community carries when people come together with love at the center of their heart – there is a special strength and bond formed amongst one another.

I felt a love that day and a sense of belonging that was unmatchable to any other time in my life. I was comforted knowing I was not walking this path alone, and that God placed these people in my life for a specific reason. These people didn't care about my beach wave blowouts or my bald head – they saw into the core of who I was and loved me for it.

At the same time, as we all laughed, smiled, and cheered one another on, I realized that this gift, an outpouring of love, was highly uncomfortable for me to receive. Every hug I gave or "thank you" I said, seemed unjustifiable in comparison to their giant act of kindness.

While every bone in my body wanted to figure out a way to generously reciprocate and thank them for their love towards me, I also understood how, at certain times in life, it is important to learn how to receive – however uncomfortable it may feel. And God knew I needed to feel this uncomfortable moment of receiving, this moment of feeling loved by others.

As we were finishing up, the teenage boys were checking themselves in the mirror and joking about the predicted reactions from the girls at school, and I stood up and gave a much-needed "thank you" speech.

Again, my words felt incomparable to their actions, but I spoke what was in my heart: I thanked them for each one of their friendships, I said how I was looking forward to making years of memories together in the future, and told them how I was truly thankful for this special day – a day that I knew I would carry in my heart, for the rest of my life.

# CHAPTER
# SEVENTEEN

A s I wrapped up one of the most memorable and emotional weekends of my life, I knew it was time for me to switch gears, as the countdown had officially begun for my third chemo treatment.

To keep my mind off things, I dove into work, preparing for the upcoming automotive conference Brian and I were hosting in Palm Beach for three-hundred people, plus, members of my family who were all flying into town.

As Brian was busy preparing presentations, scheduling speaking sessions, and reviewing content from featured speakers, I coordinated with our executive assistant, leaning on her, in all honesty more than I usually did, to help select meals, organize marketing material, staff the event, and register the sponsors and attendees.

Feeling relaxed with the event in her capable hands and less preoccupied about the minute details, I managed to allow one of my annual responsibilities to slip through the cracks.

I was at the mall, shopping to find an event outfit, when our assistant called asking if I was still planning to give the Sunday morning message. My arm froze midway through the clothing rack, realizing the whole idea had escaped my mind.

A few years ago, Brian and I had recognized that our events fell on Sundays, which meant that our attendees had to be away from their families and churches on the most important day of the week, the sabbath, so we had started hosting Sunday morning services as a way to bring church to them.

Even though we took some critical heat for this decision, as several automotive industry folks tried to discourage us from mixing business with our faith, Brian and I had felt a strong Calling to minister in *all* areas of our life.

In the past, I had preached creative and inspirational messages surrounding a specific piece of Scripture, which mostly focused on foundational principles from the Old Testament teachings – my favorite part of the Bible.

With the awkward silence between me and my assistant hanging in the air, I felt God ask me: *"This is an opportunity for you to share your journey thus far, what do you think?"*

Despite having zero content prepared, I impulsively responded. "Yes. I will do it. I will call you tomorrow with the title of my session so you can print the proper signage."

We hung up the phone and I started brainstorming and praying out loud the rest of the way through the mall.

However, the more I considered my ideas, the more I found myself having difficulty pinning down specific talking points for a twenty-minute session, as there were so many different directions I could go in.

And yet, despite all the ideas I was contemplating, as I paid for my outfit and made my way back to my car, a title kept forming in my mind:

"Thank You Cancer."

I drove home, solidifying my message and my underlying goal, part of which would be to demonstrate how even some of the hardest battles in life, such as cancer, are winnable.

I knew I also wanted to elaborate on the power behind some of the key lessons I had learned thus far such as adopting a *teachable* mentality through seeking the blessings of each day, as difficult as that practice can be; and more importantly, how leaning on God to guide the way is critical to our overall healing.

I decided I would emphasize the importance of transforming the common mindset of "why me?" to a mental posture of "teach me." I would tell how this mentality shift enabled me to obtain an unsurmountable peace – a peace that seemed to make no real sense; "*a peace which surpasses all understanding,*"[10] a peace only obtainable through a relationship with Jesus; a peace I wanted to teach others how to achieve, for I knew firsthand that when one achieves that peace within their heart, despite their circumstances, they can still win the battle.

I drove home, my presentation points strengthening in my mind, when a sliver of doubt rose up, as if a force were trying to deter me from sharing my story – as if it were trying to convince me not to be around a crowd and to wait for the next event. I immediately recognized this force as the work of the devil who would do anything to stop me from sharing God's good news.

I not only ignored his manipulative scheming tactics, but I refuted them with a stronger counter argument: I reminded myself there was a unique power in sharing my story now – while I was literally fighting through the battle – for this could create a unique form of authenticity and perhaps offer an irreplaceable, emotional connection with my audience that couldn't be obtained by sharing at a later point in my life.

As I stopped at red lights, I thumbed copious notes into my phone, outlining key points. Once home, I ran up the driveway, went into our office, grabbed my journal

10. Philippians 4:6. ESV.

and practically ran to the dining room table to record my thoughts before anything escaped my mind.

When my hand started to cramp from trying to keep up with the waterfall of words spilling from my mind, I finally took a break and looked back over everything I had written.

As I read what would become the middle of my speech, I noticed that there was a certain transition that caught my attention, a certain pause in the flow if the message, which caused me to think: *this would be a great moment to take off my wig.*

I wrestled with this idea. The first thought that came to mind was that it would be powerful and impactful, driving the message of my story home. However, my second thought was that I might scare my audience. They were not used to seeing my bald head and worse, what if they judged me?

Going back and forth between these mixed emotions, I decided that taking off my wig in public was necessary for me to do, regardless of the audience's opinions, as it would be my chance to unashamedly declare my love for myself and for God. It would also be a public affirmation of what I already believed to be true inside my heart: that God's love was all I need.

I was starting to feel comfortable with my decision and decided to do a quick read through of the speech with Brian. After I had finished reading, he said how he loved the overall message and thought my storytelling skills would be extremely impactful in resonating with the audience; then, he asked me a question:

"Would you consider taking off your wig?"

I smiled, as I felt God reaffirming my idea was in fact, the right one.

"Actually, I was thinking about it" I responded, and proceeded to paint the picture of my vision to him.

We both agreed that it would be a powerful and monumental moment for both myself and the audience, however, a piece of me struggled with the execution of the idea, as the tiny, doubtful voice inside of me thought: *will you really have the boldness to do it considering you are still adjusting to the new, buzz-cut hair style that is only days old?*

Over the next few days, as I simultaneously prepped for my third chemo treatment, I focused on resolving any last-minute needs for our conference, and on posturing my heart to be an open vessel for the Holy Spirit.

Sunday arrived, and I felt a mix of excitement and nerves stir in my body, as I stood on the wings of the stage. I knew these emotions were completely normal, so I took a moment to be still, breathe, and try to enjoy the beauty of this opportunity standing before me.

I stepped onto the stage, and to my complete surprise, my session was completely packed, so that it was standing room only.

Anxiety crept in, and I tried to remind myself that this was not about me. God had placed me there, to share my story for a reason – beyond what my mind could fully comprehend. I knew there was someone in that room or someone online that would watch the recording who needed to hear my message, someone I may never even meet.

Thinking this, I stepped forward onto the stage determined to reach that one person, no matter how uncomfortable it made me, so that I could let them know they were not alone in fighting their battle. That whatever their battle – be it a career crisis, family crisis, relationship crisis, or health crisis – there is peace and purpose in the storm.

I began speaking, and before I knew it, the twenty minutes had ended, and I found myself smiling at God for helping me achieve the perfect execution of my message.

Many people were touched by my story and especially with the moment I took off my wig. In that moment, the room went silent. It was a draw-dropping moment, as many of the people saw me for the first time without hair.

After the initial shock, I could see some of the people crying and passing tissues to one another, as the visual reminder of cancer struck their heart.

Afterwards, many people of the audience approached me afterwards to share words of gratitude and appreciation, and after the entire three-day conference had ended, one attendee texted me a special note:

*"Hi Carrie, originally, I was not planning to come to this conference, and I bought my plane ticket last minute to fly from Arizona to Florida. God clearly had a plan, and I am glad I felt the calling to come. It was His Word that I was there to hear, thank you for sharing exactly what I needed to hear!"*

"Wow!" I said to myself while reading his text, there was that *one* person.

# CHAPTER
# EIGHTEEN

I made it through my third treatment like a pro, making sure I ate right, rested, exercised, and did everything I possibly could do to prepare my body to function at its optimal level prior to the infusion.

The six-hour treatment process seemed to breeze by rather quickly, with, of course, the most uncomfortable part of the process being the hours my hands and feet had to be on ice.

December 8, 2021, the day of my last infusion, had finally arrived, and I found myself praising God for the miracle that I had made it this far without getting sick, being hospitalized, or experiencing unmanageable, negative side effects.

As I returned home after my last treatment, ready to

buckle down and endure the few days of physical exhaustion that lay ahead, I reflected on how grateful I was that I had selected the shorter path of TC treatment, as it enabled me to finish before Christmas. Moreover, I would be able to start the new year off with a clean bill of health.

2022 was looking promising in many ways: I was excited to launch my new, YouVersion, Italian devotional series in January, initiate the process of writing my second book, schedule my last reconstruction surgery for the end of February (back in New Jersey), and take a much-needed trip with my husband and parents in April.

As we planned the vacation details, we recognized that the timing of the trip would be cutting it close to the "five-week no travel" protocol after my operation, but instead of worrying if I would be healed in time, I planned as though life was moving forward. For regardless of what the future held, I had full confidence that God would help me every step of the way.

One week after my last infusion, I met with my oncologist for the last time before my three-month check-up. I shared with her my plans to travel to Europe in the Spring, and with a warm, heartfelt smile she said:

"It sounds to me like you are getting your life back."

"Yes, I feel like I am," I said.

My final reconstruction surgery was scheduled for the

end of February – just under the three-month mark post last chemo – and she assured me that that date should be no problem. She understood my urgency to get it done before my trip and before the rest of the year became occupied with other events, but more importantly, she understood my desire to close this chapter of my life.

With the final reconstruction surgery confirmed for February 28th, I flew back to my parents' house in New Jersey to quarantine, document pieces of my story, experiences, and lessons, and to work on my Italian speaking skills.

I had kept up my Italian through weekly Skype sessions with a friend who lived in Milan and my Italian language teacher who I'd met in Florence three years earlier, now living in Rome.

Through the years of studying with my teacher, she had become like family to me, and whenever Brian and I went to Italy and spent time in Rome, we always visited her and her husband to share a meal together and solidify what had become a beautiful friendship. Moreover, she and I shared a unique bond, as she had been diagnosed with cancer at the same time as me.

Hers was a completely different type of cancer, but nonetheless, there we were: two close friends, worlds apart, yet, close at heart, fighting and cheering each other on throughout every step of our battle.

As I was approaching my second surgery, I had started to feel encouraged about my cancer journey coming to a close, and I was praying the same held true for her prognosis.

Our calls had become irregular over the recent months due to our treatment schedules, so I had texted her, telling her I was looking forward to our next call so we could catch up.

The following morning, following my morning quiet time with God, I began writing, when my phone dinged with a WhatsApp alert.

The note was from my teacher, and as I read her words, my heart sank. She needed to pause our lessons she told me, as her body was not responding well to the treatments. She had been suffering from nausea, headaches, and lack of energy.

A lump formed in my throat, and I found myself feeling a mixture of sadness and guilt for having responded well to similar medications.

Feeling conflicted inside and not knowing the best way to respond, I did the only thing I could think of: I promised that I would pray for her. I also tried to infuse some positivity into the conversation, by mentioning how Brian and I would be in Italy in April and would love to see her and her husband.

She said she would love that, and so long as she was feeling good, she would love to have us over for lunch.

After our brief conversation came to an end, I found

myself sitting back in my parent's comfy, leather, club chair with her words weighing heavy on my heart.

I called Brian and told him about the conversation. He was very sad to hear the news and said he would be praying for her as well.

"We have to see her when we go Brian...Something inside of me is telling me...I know we will only be in Rome for a few hours, and if she isn't up for having lunch, we need to make a point to visit her...even if it's only for a few minutes."

"Ok, we will see what we can do," Brian responded.

While my teacher remained in my prayers every single day, I continued to stay on top of my Italian lessons with my good friend from Milan, the Campus Pastor of VIVE Church Milan who is also an excellent language teacher. in both Italian and English. On one of the calls, as we talked about potential dates to have dinner together, out of the blue, she proposed an idea. She asked me if I thought it would be possible to organize a one-day women's event at the church while I was in town. She would invite the women who were part of the church and their friends, and I could encourage the ladies by sharing a piece of my story and the intricate role my faith had played in my cancer journey. The bonus would be that I would present my story in Italian, so it would be great practice for my language skills.

I didn't know what to say. I was elated and petrified all

at once. Immediately, a voice inside of me said: "You can't do that, you are not *that* good at Italian."

And yet, without thinking it through, I agreed: "I would love to do it!"

Brian encouraged me saying that I would do a great job and told me not to worry, as my Italian skills were better than I thought, and adding: "God will equip you every step of the way, just like He has already been doing."

I felt excited about the opportunities that lay ahead, but knew I needed first to get through my upcoming surgery. I did not want to put myself under any unnecessary stress prior to the operation, so I scribbled some notes in my journal and decided to revisit things after the end of the month.

As Brian and I approached the front doors of the surgery center, we experienced a sense of déjà vu. It felt like the past six months had been condensed into one week and it was only yesterday that we were here for the first time.

With the hospital's instructions to leave all jewelry and accessories at home and bring only a form of ID and phone, I looked at Brian and said:

"I guess this means that I should leave my beanie hat here."

The soft, Gucci hat had quickly become my new "look" over the past few months, and I had developed a sentimental attachment to it.

Truth be told, I'd also come to depend upon it. The hat was not only comfortable and warm to wear, but whenever I wore sweatshirts or baggier clothes, I felt as though the beanie balanced out the look of my small head, which helped my confidence; for though I'd made one public display of my baldness, I hadn't really anticipated a repeat. And yet, with my hair starting to sprout, and my final breast surgery taking place within the next few hours, I thought that it might be a good time to let the beanie go, not just then, but going forward.

I handed the cap to Brian and walked through the sliding glass doors. One more surgery. And I hoped to walk out of that building embracing the new me from toe to head.

# CHAPTER
# NINETEEN

I opened my eyes and squinted at my surroundings in the operation waiting room, slowly coming back to my senses. A nurse walked in and approached my station to check how I was feeling.

She placed on a tray before me the standard apple juice and graham cracker remedy and said she was happy to inform me that my surgery went well.

"Do I have drains?" I asked.

She chuckled, likely at the dreaded look of panic I had on my face, and said:

"You're actually drain free!"

Feeling as though I had just won the lottery, I carefully got dressed, and called Brian to come pick me up.

Over the next few days, I was cautious with my arm movements, making sure not to raise them, or to lift "anything over five pounds" – which was essentially everything.

The protocols were the same as my first surgery, but this time, instead of weekly appointments with my plastic surgeon, I only needed just one appointment at the five-week mark – a clearance appointment with my doctor, which would be a few days before embarking on our family European trip.

Ultimately, it was the doctor's decision as to whether I would be able to travel or not. While he had previously mentioned that it would most likely not be an issue based on how well I healed from my first surgery, I was still nervous as a lot of things were at stake. If he thought I was not ready, that would not only cost my family a lot of non-refundable reservations, but I would also have to cancel my Sisterhood event and risk not being able to see my teacher.

Staying positive and praying my body would heal quickly without any complications, I busied myself with things I could do without lifting my arms: writing my book, practicing my Italian, and prepping my speech for the event in Italy.

I found myself in a similar predicament to when I was developing my presentation for our industry event in Florida and asked myself: *with everything that had happened over the past few months, what exactly do I want to speak on?*

Considering my audience would be young women, the

majority of whom I had not met before, I thought I might introduce myself by sharing a few pieces about my past – how I worked in the fashion industry in New York City, started my own handbag line, met Brian, and got involved with VIVE Church – then, I would incorporate a clip of my recent cancer journey and some advice I gleaned along the way.

As I outlined my talking points, I once again became aware that He was asking me to use my story to influence the lives of others. And for some reason, this time felt more powerful; like everything I went through, I would do it again, if I could experience that sensation of being a vessel used by God and help others through their struggles.

With the five-week mark post-surgery rapidly approaching, I started to organize my clothes, shoes, and cosmetics for our trip.

We would start the trip with my parents in Switzerland, embark on a week-long Viking canal cruise, end in Amsterdam, then after a few days there, my parents would return home and Brian and I would fly to Italy for two and a half weeks.

Even though it had only been seven months since my last trip to Italy, it had felt like years, and I was more than ready to get back there.

As I was driving to my five-week check-up appointment

with my plastic surgeon, hoping for clearance of travel considering, my mind started to wander thinking about our trip. Before I knew it, I was visualizing some of my favorite places in Italy and could literally hear the clinking espresso cups from behind a local bar, the vespa scooters passing by, and the beautiful, dramatic words of the Italian language, which was music to my ears.

Suddenly, with that thought, my Italian teacher came to mind. It had been a while since I had last heard from her, and I wondered how she was doing.

Moreover, I didn't like the fact that every time I thought of her, I got a small knot in my stomach and a sense of urgency to see her.

Even though her time zone was six hours ahead of me, and it would be the middle of the night there, I told myself to write her a message once I had reached the doctor's office.

After a few short minutes of sitting in the waiting room, the nurse called me into the examining room. My doctor was very pleased with the results and the healing of my scars and told me that I had clearance to travel.

*Excellent*, I thought. Those were the exact words I had been hoping to hear.

I thanked him so much for all the time and energy, he had poured into his work and patients – over 80% of whom were cancer patients – and he told me how it was an honor for him to have patients like myself who trust him in this way.

I chatted with his PA a few minutes longer – the one who held my hand on the OR table – as she and I had become good friends throughout this whole process. We made plans to have dinner together the next time I would be in town, and as we hugged good-bye, she wished me a great time on my trip and reminded me not to lift any luggage.

After that appointment, it felt as though everything just steamrolled ahead. I quickly became occupied with packing and running errands for our trip, that I almost forgot about making a hair appointment.

With my hair having grown a little more than an inch, I thought that it was the right time to embrace a new "do."

I was not exactly sure what that new "look" meant, but I had been going to the Lambs & Wolves Hair Salon in Red Bank, New Jersey for half my life and trusted the owner of the salon and all his stylists on staff.

As I sat in the salon chair permitting the hair stylist to have full reign in producing a "cool but classic" look for me, I could not dismiss the mixture of emotions that had begun stirring inside of me, as I reflected on the difficult moments I had experienced while sitting in different salon chairs over the past few months.

I thought about the panic attack I had while getting my hair blown out shortly after my diagnosis. I thought about how I went for blowouts after my first surgery while still having the drains connected to my sides and hidden under my clothes. And how could I forget one of the hardest moments in my life: sitting in the salon chair to have my head shaved.

However, while all these memories came flooding back, instead of feeling sad, I felt grateful, confident, and proud. I was grateful for God guiding my steps throughout the entire process and giving me the strength to endure this season in my life. I felt confident in my new skin, and proud that I had remained diligent in living out my faith throughout one of life's most difficult obstacles.

Sitting in the salon chair that day, I told myself that it was important to never forget where I came from, but at the same time, not allow the past to dictate my future.

Before I knew it, the three hours of processing my hair color had past, and I was staring at a new bleach blonde, pixie cut Carrie Pasch. Even though the blonde seemed awfully bright to me, as I was not used to that color, the stylist explained that the more my roots grew, the more it would give more texture and depth, resulting in an ideal look.

I smiled and told her how much I loved it and shared how comical I thought it was that I spent half my life trying to cover up my roots with different highlighting and dying processes, and now I was welcoming them.

As we laughed at the truth of that statement, she finished the final touches of styling my hair by taking a small scoop of hair wax, putting it the palm of her hand, and she shaped and molded my hair, she said:

"This product will be your new best friend!"

Again, I chuckled to myself thinking how humorous it was that half my bathroom cabinet was filled with different flat irons, curling irons, round brushes, and a dozen different de-frizz, straightening, and de-tangling sprays and serums, and now, all I needed was canister of wax. Life just got a little simpler for me.

I told her how my hair preparation time in the morning had drastically reduced ever since I had shaved my head, as the short hair only required a quick towel dry – forget the blow-dryer, a brush was not even needed.

We agreed that saving on preparation time was an absolute perk of a pixie cut styled cut, and we brushed the surface of the conversation surrounding the idea of making this a permanent, new "look" for me.

I told her that it was something I was considering, but that I had not decided yet. I thought that I would let it grow a little more and see how I felt in the next few months, plus, I said: "I haven't given it much thought, because I had a million other things going on and it's just hair!"

As I paid, left the salon, and got into my car to return

home, I took a moment to pause. I realized how that simple, yet profound phrase I said earlier was stuck in my mind, so I repeated it again to myself:

"It's just hair."

In that moment I realized that after all I had been through over the past few months, the thought of obsessing over my hair, like I used to do, was a foreign and somewhat silly thought. Without even knowing it, it now ranked very low on my list of priorities.

In fact, the longer I thought about the entire road I had traveled over the years – hopping from one salon chair to another, all around the world until finally reaching the one I had sat in today – I realized that there was a deeper lesson gleaned.

I had awakened to the reality that God needed to cleanse me of my own self-judgement and help me love myself without any type of makeshift wig. He wanted me to see the genuine beauty He sees in me – with hair or without hair.

As this personal truth began to seep into my soul, it became clear that the only way for me to truly accept my own natural beauty, was to have what I had idolized most taken away: my hair.

I was still in my car for a moment longer, and suddenly, found myself once again uttering, "Thank, you cancer." Only this time, I was not challenging my disease for trying to shake my faith in God. This time I was genuinely thanking it for helping me build a new, stronger version of myself.

# CHAPTER
# TWENTY

B efore I had time to blink, April 2nd, the departure day for our European extravaganza, had arrived. After mandatory testing for COVID, Brian, my parents, and I loaded up the car and headed to the JFK Airport in New York, bound for Zürich, Switzerland.

Halfway through the 8-hour flight, I stood to stretch and use the restroom. As I patiently waited for a restroom to become vacant, I smiled beneath my mask at the flight attendant who was busy preparing drinks. Beneath her mask, she smiled back as she poured a can of coke into an iced-filled glass, and I appreciated the moment, despite the gear adorning our face. And then she said:

"I love your haircut."

I was taken aback, realizing that was the first time I had received a compliment on my hair from someone who knew nothing about my past. "Thank you so much," I said.

She continued multitasking for a moment longer, and was just about to leave the galley to deliver the drink in her hand, when she stopped short and turned to face me:

"I am so sorry, but I have to ask, how old are you? You look so young with that adorable haircut."

"I am 39, and you just made my day. Not only because you think I look young, but because you simply complimented my hair which is new style for me having recently finished chemo," I said.

She took a step closer to me and pulled her mask down. "You truly look amazing," she said. "I had no idea you just had cancer."

"Don't worry...I mean it– you really made my day," I said, genuinely. Even though many different friends and family members had complimented my new hair, the flight attendant's compliment –kind words from a perfect stranger – were the ones I knew I'd never forget.

At the same time, I found the moment somewhat laughable, as I thought to myself, that I rarely ever received compliments on any one of my hundreds of blowouts.

\*\*\*

We landed in Zürich and spent the next two days acclimating to the European time zone. Brian, my parents, and I were excited to be in Europe together again for the first-time post-COVID, and over meals, we excitedly discussed the schedule of our Rhine River cruise for the next week. The plan was to start in France, meander through different cities in Germany, and end in the Netherlands.

The day arrived and we embarked with about 200 other passengers to cruise through the narrow canals, venture out for daily excursions, and enjoy different cuisines. In the meantime, as much fun as I was having, I made time each morning to prepare for the women's event.

I was only ten days away from my first Italian speaking event, and I wanted everything to feel perfect and polished. This included the flow of my story, my pronunciation of Italian words, and, most importantly, the authenticity and engagement of my delivery.

By the time our cruise had docked at its final port in Amsterdam, my speech was closer to where I wanted it to be, but not fully there yet either. I decided to enjoy for a bit, as we explored the Venice-like, canal city – and then, the first segment of our trip had come to an end. It was time for my parents to board their flight back to New Jersey.

I felt sad to see my parents go and felt a mild sense of unease, but I knew the feeling was not only about my speech being perfect. My parent's departure signaled that Brian and I, would now make our way to Italy – where I hoped my teacher would be well enough for us to reunite.

We made sure my parents were all set at their international terminal at Schipol Airport, then headed to the domestic terminal for our flight.

The flight to Milan was short and uneventful. We landed, claimed our bags, hailed a taxi to the hotel, checked into our room, then spent the next few days visiting with our good friends – many of whom I had not seen since my diagnosis.

After a few days in Milan, Brian and I had originally planned to spend four days at our home in Tuscany (the days prior to my speaking engagement). However, as we reviewed the schedule, we realized that I would only be able to stay two days with Brian, and then return to Milan for the Sisterhood event.

Since it would be a five-hour drive between Milan and Montalcino, the location of our house, we both agreed that would be too much travel time in too short of a time frame.

While trying to figure out the best solution, an idea suddenly came to my mind which I proposed to Brian:

"What if I stay with our friends here in Milan for the week and you still go to Montalcino. Of course, I want to see our house, but if I stay here, I can really immerse myself into the language, and ultimately, be more comfortable in speaking by the time the event rolls around."

Even though this would mean that Brian and I would have to spend a week apart, Brian agreed that it was a good idea. He fully supported my motivation and passion to pursue new ways in strengthening my Italian speaking skills, and I was truly grateful for that. Plus, I liked the fact that he would still go, relax, and spend time at our beautiful home in Tuscany. I didn't want to take that time away from him.

I ran the plan by my friends, who are pastors at VIVE Church, to make sure it was alright that I intruded into their life for the following five days, and without hesitation, they welcomed me into their home with open arms.

Living with my friends was a great experience, as it was so nice to be able to walk alongside of them and be an extra set of hands at the VIVE Church Milan office, share delicious meals together, speak Italian 24/7, and most of all, meet the wonderful people of their community.

With each day bringing a new set of experiences, the week seemed to fly by, and before I knew it, the day of the Sisterhood event was only a few hours away.

Before going to bed, I thought about my teacher and wondered how she was doing. I grabbed my phone and texted her to let her know I was looking forward to seeing her. I waited a few seconds to see if she was typing back, but there was no indication.

I decided to stay up a little longer and see if she would respond, so in the meantime, I practiced my presentation one last time, prayed, and relaxed in the comfort of my friend's couch.

As I sat, periodically checking my phone for an update on WhatsApp, I could not help but reflect on how much God had done in my life to bring me to this very moment.

Suddenly, in that emotional and reflective moment, I tossed my phone to the side, impulsively got off the couch, went into the bathroom. I turned on the light and took a good look at myself in the mirror.

I looked at my short, blonde hair, my pink-toned cheeks, the pronounced black eyeliner outlining my bottom lids – the only form of make-up I never leave home without – and I smiled to myself while thinking: *Carrie, God has brought you right here, in this moment, for a reason. You will do great tomorrow! Go and glorify Him!*

That moment in the mirror not only reflected my newly, appreciated self-beauty, but reinforced the revelation of how this life is not about living for me, rather, living for Him.

That reflective moment also drew to the surface a powerful reminder about my entire cancer experience: even though I had experienced a touch of death knocking at my front door, it had done nothing but add kindle to the burning flame inside of me to never stop living for God.

The truth of God's Word echoed in my heart:

*"Whatever you do, work at it with all your heart, as working for the Lord, not for human masters."*[11]

I smiled at myself, flipped off the bathroom light switch, and made my way back to the couch.

As I assumed my comfortable seated position, I anxiously checked my phone, hoping there would be a message from my teacher. Nothing.

I sat there staring at my blank phone screen for a moment longer, all the while refusing to acknowledge the knot inside my stomach, I quickly grabbed my computer, as I had one last thing to do before going to bed.

I had a scheduled call with my dear friend and pastor who lives in California and thought how it was perfect timing for us to chat. I could not only ask for her advice about my event the following day, but in that moment, I could also use some uplifting words of encouragement.

We spent a few minutes catching up and I shared with her how I was both excited and slightly nervous, as it was my first time presenting in Italian.

She reassured me that those feelings were both normal and healthy to have prior to any type of preaching or teaching of a message. However, before finishing our call, she took a

---

11. Colossians 3:23. NIV.

moment to share an insightful, spiritual truth that remained on my heart long after the phone conversation had ended:

"Carrie," she said, "Remember, God rewards preparation. And I know you, I know that you are well prepared."

After hearing those words, I felt a little lighter, calmer, and less anxious about needing to execute everything perfectly. I knew I was prepared – probably over prepared – now, all I needed to do was pray, and invite the Holy Spirit to guide my words in the way *He* needed them to be delivered to my audience.

I thanked her for her words of wisdom and encouragement, and we hung up our FaceTime call.

Feeling a slight high of excitement for the new day that lay ahead, I decided it was time to get some rest, and that having heard no news from my teacher was good news.

Going to bed, I felt ready and prepared in every way possible. However, what I was not ready for, was a series of events that would soon take place and make one of the happiest days of my life, also one of the saddest.

# CHAPTER

# TWENTY ONE

The Sisterhood event exceeded my expectations, and the VIVE Milan team did an incredibly tasteful job on bringing a flare of Spring into the air through all their floral arrangements and pastel color décor.

My heart skipped a beat as the doors opened at 9:30AM and the women began to trickle in. The first thirty minutes were designated for socializing over coffee and a light breakfast, and then at 10:00AM, everyone was asked to take their seats.

As the ladies got comfortable and the chatter started to transition into silence, I took a seat next to the Campus Pastor of VIVE Milan at the front of the room.

She welcomed all the ladies, gave a brief introduction

about me, and just like that, our interview was underway.

Since I knew the questions in advance, the first one being a brief description about myself and snapshot of my past as a handbag designer, I noticed that midway through my response, I was talking a faster than usual and reminded myself to take my time.

Slowing down my words helped me to not rush through my pronunciations, but more importantly, prevented me from doing what I feared the most – sounding scripted.

As I finished my response, I decided to force myself to take a moment to pause, so I decided to reach for the glass of water sitting on the table, behind a small plant next to me.

As I started to lift the glass, my hand started to uncontrollably shake, and the water wobbled from side to side within the glass.

Immediately, I decided it was not a good idea to try to have a sip and possibly spill water all over myself. So, I cautiously placed it back on the table, and instead, casually adjusted the position of my legs in order to distract people from the possibility of seeing my trembling hand.

Before responding to the second question, I consciously took a deep breath, relaxed my shoulders, and told myself to stop being nervous and enjoy the moment that I had worked so hard towards.

From that point forward, I became more comfortable,

confident, and present in the moment. I was less focused on having perfect speaking skills, and more in tune with leaning into what the Holy Spirit was guiding me to say to the specific group of ladies that were sitting in front of me.

To say God showed up and guided me would be an understatement.

The more I shared my story, the more I felt a special connection with the ladies and was beyond thrilled to witness the feeling being reciprocated as they laughed, cried, and leaned into my story with open hearts.

It wasn't long before the atmosphere of the room shifted from what seemed as though was initially a room full of strangers and transformed into a group of women sharing a common bond – like that of sisters.

The forty minutes seemed to fly by, and suddenly, my friend had arrived at the last question.

At the end of the interview, we all took a few minutes to pray with one another, then, after taking some photos and individually conversing with some of the ladies, I snuck away to call Brian.

He was on his way from Montalcino to Florence and had been anxiously waiting to receive my call and hear how everything went.

I couldn't say much before the tears of joy started streaming down my face, and I got choked up while trying to tell him all the details.

Not wanting to ruin my makeup, I quickly regrouped, and told him how well everything went. I emphasized how great it felt to make an intimate connection with an audience in another language – that was what I had prayed for the most – and how, for me, it was an actual miracle that God had been equipping me for all these years as I learned Italian for this very moment. I felt humbled and honored to be serving Him in this way.

Brian was elated to hear the news and the happiness in my voice and told me that he couldn't wait to see me and give me a big hug and kiss.

After we exchanged an "I love you," I hung up the phone and made my way back out to help the girls tidy up.

Once everything was organized, it was time to head back to my friend's house, so we got in the car and started the thirty-minute drive back to their home.

It felt good to relax in the back seat and allow my mind and body to recoup from the rush of adrenaline it had been experiencing throughout the past few hours.

Without thinking twice, I reached for my phone inside my purse and checked the alerts and updates. Nothing pressing appeared on the home screen, and I quickly realized that it was still the early hours of the morning on the east coast of the United States. However, that didn't prevent me from texting my parents, as I wanted them to wake up to the great news of my event.

After I sent the message within our small group chat, my phone rang, and my stomach tightened at the name that appeared at the top of the screen.

It was my Italian teacher. *She never calls me*, I thought to myself. *We always text.*

Something about this phone call told me it was not good, but at the same time, I was thinking to to myself: *What if she just needs to adjust our preliminary lunch plans and preferred calling instead of texting.*

I debated on whether I should answer or text her and ask if I could call her back when I was in a more private setting.

I went with my initial instinct that this call was something important, so I asked my friends to turn down the volume of the radio, and I answered the phone:

"Ciao!" I said, in my energetic and upbeat voice.

"Ciao Carrie," responded the voice on the other end, but it was not the voice of my teacher. It was her husband.

My heart sank deeper into my chest as I confirmed that I was in a quiet place in which I could talk. He proceeded to tell me that she was not doing well and updated me with a series of events that had taken place over the previous weeks. He said that he was so upset to be sharing this news with me, but he wanted me to know the details about her condition since she and I shared a special relationship together.

I asked him if he thought that it would still be possible for me and Brian to see her in two days when we arrived in Rome. He said that he was unsure of how much time she had left, but he would keep me informed on any changes.

I thanked him for his call and hung up the phone, streaming tears, feeling the heavy weight of sorrow, and also the precariousness of life.

Just a few months earlier, my friend had been doing well. And just a few hours earlier, I had considered this day to be one of the most exciting and memorable days of my life – all thanks to her friendship and her teaching; now it was also memorable for the completely opposite reason.

Mulling through all the different thoughts in my mind, I couldn't help but think of how proud she would be to hear how I spoke to a room full of women *all in Italian*. I certainly would not be where I was without her.

I stared out the window, watching the landscapes of many cities along the Italian Autostrada (highway) breeze by, and started to pray. I thanked God for my teacher's life, our friendship, and the great impact she had made on my life. I told Him how sad I was that this was happening to her and for peace in her and her husband's hearts.

At some point during my ongoing, silent conversation with God, I felt compelled to make a promise to my teacher and requested that He deliver a specific message to her on my behalf. I said,

"Simona, I promise to proudly carry your torch forward – I promise to continue spreading your love for the Italian language."

And then, I got to work on making it to Rome faster, so I could see her.

***

After what seemed like a grueling forty-eight hours later, Brian and I pulled up in front of our hotel in Rome. As he unloaded the bags and checked in, I texted my teacher's husband to see if it was still possible for us to come over.

It was 6:00PM and he had previously mentioned that someone else was coming to visit in the evening. I told him how I would love to see the two of them before we flew out early the next morning, and within a few minutes, he responded telling us it was alright to come over.

The twenty-minute taxi ride felt like twenty hours, as I anxiously sat in the back seat fidgeting at every red light.

When we finally arrived at their apartment, we were greeted by their adorable cocker spaniel dog and took a few minutes to talk with her husband alone before being brought into the bedroom where Simona was resting.

I sat down on the chair by her bedside with one goal in mind: to bring a smile to her face. No matter how easy it would be for me to succumb to the sadness of the situation, I focused on bringing my energetic self to into the room to make her laugh and smile.

I started talking to her in Italian, and we chatted as two old friends would over a cup of cappuccino at a local cafe. She asked how I was feeling after my second surgery and chemo treatments, and we shared a laugh over our new, matching, short hair styles.

I told her about my event, and she was so happy to hear it went well and told me how proud she was of me.

After about twenty minutes of conversation, I heard the front door of their apartment open, which indicated another guest had arrived. That was my cue that it was time to leave. But I wanted to stay. I wanted to stay because this was my first time seeing my friend in three years. And I wanted to stay because I didn't know how to leave.

How do you say good-bye to someone you know you will not see again? I smiled at her sweet face and sent a direct SOS prayer up to God to give me the right words to speak before leaving the room.

I told her how grateful I was that God brought us together and how I would not be where I was today without her.

I told her how much I loved her.

I told her how I will forever cherish our time together.

And then, like quicksand, the moment to leave had arrived. I could not say "good-bye." Instead, I said that I would see her one day soon.

As Brian and I exited the apartment building and stepped out onto the sidewalk, we were immediately hit with a rush of uncharacteristically warm air for an early spring evening. Sunset was beginning, seeming to burn majestically across the city in bright, transparent beams of light, radiating God's infinite Glory.

I intentionally stopped and took a moment to be still.

In that moment of complete stillness, I noticed how my senses were in tune with the vast, natural beauty that surrounded me: the colors of the Pinus Pinea, Rome's iconic stone pine trees that resembled large, umbrella-like structures. Clusters of these trees lined the far horizon, coloring the landscape with a vibrant green hue. From them, came the high-pitched songs of the birds, growing louder and more pronounced as my ears opened to them. I could hear, too, the nearby shopkeeper chatting with his friend as he cleaned his sidewalk, preparing, like most of the city, to close up shop for the day. In the waning day, it felt as though the world was pausing to reflect upon the beauty, goodness, peace, and the simplicity of life.

While my heart was grieving for my friend, having taken that moment to be still and soak in God's ever-present beauty, I felt like I was standing between the two worlds of life and death.

"Are you ready?" Brian asked, and I nodded.

We began to walk towards the nearest taxi stand. Finally, Brian broke the silence and asked:

"Can I ask what is running through your mind?"

I turned towards him and finally uttered the two-word, question I'd wondered in the beginning of this journey. Only now, the question was not framed in punishment, but in the concept of destiny:

"*Why me?* I mean, why am I still here...and she is..." I couldn't bear to finish the statement.

"I don't know..." He responded, "But maybe...maybe because God is not done with you yet."

While I am sure he meant to speak those words in a comforting manner, I couldn't help but feel a slight sting to my ears as the words fell from his mouth.

"I feel bad...It just feels unfair...," I responded.

He continued, "We all have our time, and none of us know when that time will come, so we have to live each day like it is our last."

Of course, I was familiar with that truth, but something about hearing it right then made it hit a little harder being that I was quite literally experiencing the reality of the situation. Perhaps, it was true that while my teacher was being called to return to her heavenly home and into God's warm, embrace – stretching like the sun's endless rays across the horizon – I was being called to remain here, on this temporary earth, to keep living for reasons that were still unknown to me.

As we reached the taxi stand and started our drive back to the hotel, the conflicting emotions of pain and peace wrestled inside my heart, until a heaviness settled. At the same time, I knew that as painful as the past twenty-four hours had been, God's timing was always perfect, as it had truly been a miracle that He had helped me persevere through my cancer battle throughout the previous eight months, and bring me here, to Rome, to allow my path to cross one last time with my dear friend.

As the remaining hours of our trip came to a close, and that *why me?* question of destiny floated inside my thoughts, I accepted the fact that I would never know the true answer to that question. Only God, the author of our lives, would ever know that answer.

While the thought of not knowing my future or exact time of death felt like a difficult and daunting truth to tackle, the more I meditated on that thought, the more I felt peace in my heart, because I knew that as long as I was still living, I was serving a *good* God. A God who loves me, who has a good plan for my life, and who wants to see me thrive and live life to my fullest potential.

My journey to date has taught me that having a close relationship with God doesn't guarantee a life without pain, as we live in a fallen and broken world, but it does guarantee a source of eternal peace within the pain.

I learned that my time on earth is precious, and that instead of being scared by that fact, I am inspired to live.

I learned that committing myself faithfully to God allows me to distinguish between a voice of opposition or opportunity.

I learned that there is always purpose in the pain, and as difficult as it is to discover its meaning, it is possible so long as one maintains a *teachable* heart.

# ACKNOWLEDGMENTS

I would first like to thank my loving husband, Brian Pasch, and parents, Robin and Joseph Hemphill. This was a journey I could not have done without the three of you by my side. Your infinite love and support, throughout all seasons of my life, have forever marked my heart. Thank you for being you.

In addition to my family, this journey would not have been possible without the incredible team of doctors in my life. I would like to thank the wonderful medical teams and staff at Cooperman Barnabas Medical Center in Livingston, New Jersey, Short Hills Surgery Center in Millburn, New Jersey, Memorial Sloan Kettering Cancer Center in New York, New York, Weill Cornell Medicine in New York, New York, and the Lynn Cancer Institute in Boca Raton, Florida, with special recognition to Dr. Cyrus Loghmanee, Dr. Michelle Blackwood, Dr. Linda Vahdat, Dr. Tiffany Traina, Dr. Jennifer Wagmiller,

Dr. Jane Skelton, Dr. Nitin Sethi, Angela Monterosso, and Priscilla Lawrence. You are not only extraordinary doctors and medical professionals in your field, but exceptional people at heart. I am honored to be your patient. Thank you for caring for me.

I could not allow one more page to flip by without taking a moment to thank my dear friend and editor, or whom I refer to as the "director of my book," Heather Siegel. Thank you so much for investing your time and energy into this project. Your professional expertise helped guide my writing, encouraging my storytelling skills, and hold me accountable in achieving my set deadlines. Thank you for everything.

Luca Frezza, I cannot thank you enough for your willingness to dive head first into this project and translate my book into Italian, so that my story could be shared with the people I love. Our timeline was tight, but that did not stop your servant heart – thank you!

Pastor Wendy Perez, thank you so much for your encouragement, support, and advice during this season of my life. Your coaching sessions have been a source of creativity, motivation, and inspiration for me, and I truly cherish our friendship. Thank you again for the kind words in the Foreword of this book.

Pastors Adam and Keira Smallcombe and the entire VIVE Church family – thank you for your consistent love, support, prayers, and encouragement in my life. Despite living miles apart, the contagious love instilled within the entire VIVE community, makes me proud and grateful to call you my family…my church home. Love you all.

Pastor Christian Andrews, this book would not exist if it wasn't for you obeying the prompting in your heart to pray that bold prayer over my life when this journey first began – the prayer where you requested that I become *teachable* to God during my cancer journey. This is a true testament to the power of prayer and how God hears the smallest prayer, and furthermore, how it can have a ripple effect throughout one's life. Without your prayer, my perspective and experiences would not have been the same, and this book would not be here today. Thank you for helping me re-establish my faith from the very beginning and become *teachable* by God.

To all my friends – with a special shout-out to the head shaving crew – I want to thank you from the bottom of my heart for your love and support throughout this entire process. Every single one of your texts, emails, phone calls, cards, and social media comments, messages, posts, and "likes" have greatly impacted my life. I am truly grateful for the ways in which you have lifted me up when I needed it most and continually challenge me to keep moving forward. Every single one of your voices holds a special place in my heart, thank you.

Simona Ciarrocchi, thank you for being the best teacher and friend that a passionate, Italian student from American could ask for. I miss you dearly.

—

Made in the USA
Monee, IL
21 October 2022